Lecture Notes in Biomathematics

Managing Editor: S. Levin

9

Neil Dubin

A Stochastic Model
for Immunological Feedback
in Carcinogenesis:
Analysis and Approximations

Springer-Verlag
Berlin · Heidelberg · New York 1976

Author

Neil Dublin
New York University Medical Center
Institute of Environmental Medicine
550 First Avenue
New York, N. Y. 10016/USA

Library of Congress Cataloging in Publication Data

Dublin, Neil, 1949-
  A stochastic model for immunological feedback in
carcinogenesis.

  (Lecture notes in biomathematics ; 9)
  Bibliography: p.
  1. Carcinogenesis--Immunological aspects--
Mathematical models. 2. Tumors--Immunological aspects--
Mathematical models. 3. Approximation theory.
4. Stochastic processes. I. Title. II. Series.
RC268.5.D8   616.9'94'071   76-18930

AMS Subject Classifications (1970): 41A45, 60–03, 60J80, 60J85, 65C05, 92–03, 92A05

ISBN 3-540-07786-3 Springer-Verlag Berlin · Heidelberg · New York
ISBN 0-387-07786-3 Springer-Verlag New York · Heidelberg · Berlin

Printing and binding: Beltz Offsetdruck, Hemsbach/Bergstr.

Abstract

The main body of this research is concerned with deriving and evaluating approximations to a nonlinear stochastic birth and death process for which an exact solution in closed form is not obtained. Said stochastic process arose in a consideration of tumor growth with immunological feedback. In addition to the usually postulated constant birth and death rate for tumor cells, there is a density-dependent term in the death transition probability corresponding to the immunological response of the normal tissue against the colony of tumor cells.

Included is a discussion of previous tumor models and the biological considerations which result in the formulation of the present more mathematically complex case. The mathematical model is presented, as well as known properties of the exact stochastic process. A detailed analysis of existing approximation techniques is given; and a new method is derived which linearizes the transition probabilities of the original stochastic process to tractable form.

A simulation study was made to help evaluate the results of the various approximations, with emphasis upon the author's linearizing method. A comparison was also made of exact vs. approximate results for the quadratic death process, a simpler but still nonlinear stochastic process, for which an exact solution is obtained. A section is included on the collective model for tumor growth, with some limited properties derived.

Attention is called to the fact that, for a stochastic process modelling problem in which an approximation is used, the error is two-fold: approximation vs. model and model vs. reality. The scope here is primarily restricted to the former, although the latter is given qualitative consideration.

TABLE OF CONTENTS

LIST OF TABLES

Page

ACKNOWLEDGMENTS

Thanks are primarily due to Dr. Vincent Gallucci for his patience and thoroughness in reviewing my research, as well as for playing a constructive devil's advocate in our many conversations.

I must also thank Dr. Edward Perrin for directing me towards stochastic models for carcinogenesis in the first place and, in addition, Drs. Douglas Chapman and the late Gerald Paulik for invaluable training in modelling and applied statistics.

The bulk of this research was completed as partial fulfillment for the requirements of the Ph.D. degree while the author was supported by an N.I.H. Biometry Training Grant in the Biomathematics Group at the University of Washington. In addition, I am grateful to Dr. Bernard Pasternack for making time available to me to work on the final manuscript while at New York University Medical Center.

For their patient typing, credit is due Ms. Carolyn Nelson for the original dissertation, Mrs. Jeanette Greene for the revisions, and Miss Aimée Miranda for the final manuscript.

Finally, I would like to thank Dr. Simon Levin for his many pertinent suggestions in revising this manuscript.

1. Introduction

Stochastic processes often pose the difficulty that, as soon as a model deviates from the simplest kinds of assumptions, the differential equations obtained for the density and the generating functions become mathematically formidable. Worse still, one is very often led to equations which have no known solution and don't yield to standard analytical methods for differential equations.

In the model considered here, one for tumor growth with an immunological response from the normal tissue, a nonlinear term in the transition probability for the death of a tumor cell leads to the above-mentioned complications. Despite the mathematical disadvantages of this nonlinearity, we are able to consider a more sophisticated model biologically. Ultimately, in order to achieve a more realistic representation of a complicated phenomenon, it is necessary to examine mechanisms which allow the model to deviate from the more mathematically tractable linear format. Thus far, stochastic models for tumor growth have almost exclusively considered linear transition probabilities.

Once nonlinearity is incorporated into a model's assumptions, and intractable differential equations are encountered, it is natural to attempt some kind of approximate solution to the exact equations. But then the modelling problem becomes two-fold. Not only must one consider the discrepancy between the model and reality, but between the model and the approximate solution as well.

The scope of this research is limited to the model-approximation error. Many approximation techniques have been proposed in the past, but seldom if ever have they undergone comprehensive analysis with respect to a nonlinear process. Further, a new method is derived which linearizes the transition probabilities of a nonlinear process into those of a linear process that can be solved. Only a few of the methods turn out to be useful. Of course, an evaluation of the closeness of an approximation to the model cannot be determined exactly since the exact model is not solved. There are, nevertheless, criteria available, including stationary distributions, qualitative considerations, the deterministic solution, and Monte Carlo simulation studies. A section is included on the behavior of the author's approximation technique for a process that can be described exactly. In order to view the problem in the context of current research, we begin with a review of other models and statistical studies of carcinogenesis.

2. Background of Statistical Studies of Carcinogenesis

What follows is a review of generally recent, significant statistical work in the study of carcinogenesis. We consider not only those models, like the one developed in this work, which consider tumor growth on the cellular clone level, but also kinetic models on the scale of molecular biology and models on the so-called somatic scale, concerned with survival. The discussion is loosely grouped under the following headings: (i) Multi-hit versus single hit, multi-stage versus single stage; (ii) Multi-cell versus single cell formation; (iii) Models with stochastic growth parameters; (iv) Dose-response and survival models; (v) Goodness-of-fit considerations; (vi) Kinetic models; (vii) Breast cancer models; and (viii) Leukemia models.

A. Multi-hit versus single hit; multi-stage versus single stage; multi-cell versus single cell

Reviews of statistical studies on the cellular clone level were given by Armitage and Doll (1961) and Neyman and Scott (1967). No attempt to duplicate that effort will be made here; however, the salient points will be presented. What is central to the studies in the above-mentioned review papers is a consideration of one hit versus multi-hit and one stage versus multi-stage phenomena. The hit refers to the interaction between the carcinogen, or cancer-inducing agent, and the normal cell, resulting in the mutation of that normal cell to a cancer cell. Multi-hit means that more than one hit is necessary to effect the mutation of a normal cell. The number of stages is the number of mutations required to produce a cancer cell. A mutation results in a stage during which the mutated cell is subject to repro-duction, death, and possibly further mutation to the next stage. Arley and Iversen (1952) and Iversen (1961), to whom the earliest probabilistic model is attributed, consider a one hit, one stage mutation hypothesis. A hit between the carcinogenic agent and a normal cell results in mutation to a cancer cell, which in turn gives rise to a clone of cancer cells. The alternatives are multi-hit and multi-stage mechanisms. Multi-hit describes a mechanism in which a minimum of $\kappa > 1$ hits on the same cell are required to induce mutation. Multi-stage mechanisms postulate several successive mutations, each generating a clone of mutant cells. Thus, in a two-stage hypothesis, the first mutation leads to a clone of benign cells subject to a second order mutation resulting in malign, or cancer, cells.

A consideration of the k hit, one stage mutation hypothesis was given by Nordling (1953) and Stocks (1953), as quoted by Armitage and Doll (1957), Tucker (1961), and Neyman and Scott (1967). The latter paper presents that mechanisms as a possible explanation of the following phenomenon observed by Shimkin and Polissar (1955) and Shimkin et al. (1967) in research on lung tumors in mice: after an injection of the carcinogen (urethane), modified cells appears, increase to a maximum, and then decline. Malignant tumor nodules are present at the same time, but appear with a delay. Shimkin and Polissar suggested that the hyperplastic foci (the modified cells) and the tumors were not independent of each other, but, rather, that as some hyperplastic foci attained a certain approximate age and size, they changed into tumors. Neyman and Scott postulate the observed hypercellularity as a first stage precursor to cancer, leading via mutation to malignant tumors. The two stages are regarded mathematically as simple birth and death processes; the first is subcritical [λ (birth rate) < μ (death rate)], whereas the second is super-critical ($\lambda > \mu$). They find the implications of the two-stage theory are consistent with hypercellularity if the theory is revised so that the hit of carcinogen on a normal cell results in the mutation of its daughter cells rather than itself. Also discussed are the dose-response relationships for the various models, with emphasis on the dependence of incidence rate on time patterns of dose administration. However, Neyman and Scott are not able to validate or refute any of the models quantitatively. Klonecki (1965) develops a method of numerical calculation of the joint distribution of the number of hyperplastic foci and tumors from which a comparison of the theoretical to the empirical correlation could be made. Unfortunately, as Neyman and Scott point out, experimental data on the joint distribution is difficult to obtain. White (1972) casts doubt as to whether one can assume, as Neyman and Scott do, the number of tumors initiated is proportional to the total dose of carcinogen. The phenomenon is investigated for urethane-induced lung cancer in mice.

In a later paper, Klonecki (1970) considers, on a theoretical level, the identifiability of one-branching from multi-branching mechanisms. Branching refers to the number of tumors that can arise from a single hit of carcinogen. Hits are assumed to be Poisson-distributed. Incorporated into the formulation is a consideration of varying susceptibilities among experimental animals. Klonecki finds that the two mechanisms can be distinguished only if the distribution of susceptibility is finite. Alternatively, if the number of tumors that can be initiated by a single hit is presumed bounded, with no assumption about susceptibility, distinguishability is preserved.

Alling (1971) studied estimation of hit number for viral systems that could have application to carcinogenesis. Several different estimators of hit number are derived, including maximum likelihood, minimum chi-square, regression, and one devised by the author. In a follow-up paper, Kalbfleisch and Sprott (1974) estimate hit number by factoring the joint likelihood function which, unlike the methods in Alling's paper, do not rely on asymptotic properties or mathematical approximations.

Both O'N. Waugh (1961) and Iyer and Saksena (1970) examine tumor growth in the two-stage model where probabilities of cell division and cell loss are dependent on the age of the cell. In the latter paper, the rate of transformation of normal cells to malignant cells and expected tumor size are evaluated for different sets of the parameters.

The question of multi-cell versus single cell origin of tumors has aroused some interest. Superficially, the results of Linder and Gartler (1967), in an experiment with leiomyoma of the uterus, indicated a single cell origin, since the cells in the tumors were all of one type in females heterozygous for a certain trait. However, Buhler (1967) demonstrated that, even if the tumors were multi-cell in origin, the results could be explained by chance alone, without even so much as taking into account natural selection.

B. Dose-response and survival models

The following two studies, by Pike and Roe (1963) and Gart (1965) represent initial attempts at adapting life-table methods and the concept of dose-response curves to cancer work. Pike and Roe apply the use of a standard actuarial method to allow for non-tumor related deaths in computing the probability of being tumor-free in a given interval. Death from a tumor is defined as occurring with the appearance of a first papilloma (or malignancy), so that survivorship is based on being tumor-free.

Gart (ibid.) presents a graphical method to distinguish between two models for the relationship between dose and response over time. Note that the models are very general, not applicable solely to carcinogenesis. The "Collective Action Model" defines response, in our context, as occurring when the total number of cancer cells in a tissue exceeds a certain number. On the other hand, the "Individual Action Model" defines response as occurring when any single tumor in the tissue reaches a critical size. In either case Gart assumes that at time zero the cancer cells are Poisson distributed through the tissue and that they subsequently multiply according to an identical growth process. He finds, for large doses, approximate linear relationships between incubation time and dosage that would enable one to decide which of the models considered is appropriate. The results are applied to two viral systems.

Pike (1966) discusses three asymptotic distributions for time to occurrence of cancer in an individual tissue (the number of cells in the tissue is presumed large) and their possible application to various models of carcinogenesis. For each distribution, it is assumed that (i) the cancer begins in an individual cell, and (ii) the behavior of individual cells in a tissue is independent of one another. He derives maximum likelihood estimates for the parameters of one of the distibutional forms, which follows a Weibull probability law. Derivation of the estimates is illustrated for data from an experiment on rat vaginal cancer, and a chi-square test displays a good fit of the model to the experiment. For a physical interpretation of the parameters of this model, see Armitage and Doll (1954). It is noted that, due to the functional form of the asymptotic distribution for time to occurrence of first cancer, the model would be likely to be most successful in analyzing experiments with regularly applied carcinogen.

Lee (1970) explores further the allowance for non-tumor mortality in comparing relative carcinogenicity in skin-painting experiments. The method here is more general than that of Pike and Roe (1963), which is included as a special case. Lee combines life-table methods with the concepts of a "simulated population," i.e., one in which tumor mortality is estimated from the "actual population" of experimental animals, and non-tumor mortality is taken from a so-called "standard population." The choice of standard population depends on whether one is interested in comparing treatments or testing a theoretical model. Some examples of application are given.

Lee and O'Neill (1971) combine the technique of Pike (1966) and Lee (1970) to fit the Weibull distribution to time to first tumor in two series of mouse skin-painting experiments. Further, they postulate that the incidence rate of tumors and infiltrating carcinomas is proportional both to dose squared and adjusted time, from the start of skin-painting, to the power of k, a constant. Goodness-of-fit of the Weibull model with this additional restriction is demonstrated. More support for the use of the Weibull distribution can be found in Peto, Lee, and Paige (1972). Discussed at length are the advantages of the Weibull as compared to the lognormal model for carcinogenesis, and the superior fit of the former in the case of an experiment in mouse carcinogenesis is demonstrated.

Peto and Lee (1973) present an extension of the techniques to be found in Pike (1966). The approach is generalized by allowing one of the parameters to vary among the animals in any given group, in effect allowing for varying susceptibility, and maximum likelihood estimates for the parameters are derived. Peto and Lee point out that the derivation of these estimates depends on what can be assumed about the parameters, resulting in several different subsequent courses of action. Multiple regression is used to evaluate dose-response relationships and relative carcinogenicity of treatments.

See Peto (1974) for overall guidelines to the analysis of mortality in carcinogenesis experiments.

Berry (1975) approaches two design problems under acceptance of the Weibull model for carcinogenesis. In the first, he uses a return per unit cost approach to determine the optimal sacrifice time for animals in the experiment. Return is measured in terms of the accuracy of the estimated tumor rate, and he finds it optimal to allow each animal to die of natural causes. The second design problem involves determining the effect of delaying first exposure to the carcinogen; taken into consideration are total sample size, relative size of the delayed group, and length of the delay period. Berry notes that, although the Weibull model is generally restricted in application to continuous carcinogenesis experiments (see Pike, 1966), data from an experiment involving a single injection of asbestos have been shown to fit the Weibull distribution (Berry and Wagner, 1969).

The above studies concern themselves with experimental carcinogenesis and the appropriateness of (primarily) the Weibull model. Cook, Doll, and Fellingham (1969) consider the Weibull model in relation to human incidence data from cancer regis-tries. The Weibull, where incidence increases proportionally to a power of age, is demonstrated to better fit the data than the Gompertz equation, where incidence is assumed equal to the exponential function raised to a linear function of time. Since the Weibull does not adequately fit the data in a majority of cases, several modifications are considered. Substitution of time since first exposure to the carcinogen for age was found to work for data for cancer of the prostrate. Elimi-nated from consideration is the possibility that deviations are due to reduction of the pool of susceptibles, but temporal changes in the amount of carcinogen are suggested to explain the deviation from the Weibull model. The need for experimen-tal data to evaluate this possibility is indicated. Finally, the question is raised whether the value of one of the Weibull parameters, the power of age since first exposure, may be characteristic of the tissue affected. Examination of the data is suggestive but inconclusive. Doll (1971) continues his investigation of human incidence data with special emphasis on lung cancer.

Chang (1970) addresses the question of dose-dependence of the means and variance of survival time in an experiment in which mouse lymphoma is induced by inoculation with tumor cells. A previous study by Maryuma and Brown (1964) hypothesized exponential growth of tumor cells resulting in the death of the host at some threshold number of tumor cells. Chang investigates several possible explanations for the observed decrease in variation in survival time. It is found that a model assuming a lognormal distribution for the time it takes for the number of tumor cells to double in the host adequately explains the phenomenon of interest. An additional assumption that the number of inoculated tumor cells that generate clones is Poisson distributed does not improve the fit of the model.

Consideration is given by Kneale (1971) to the problem of estimating the respective age distributions of radiogenic and non-radiogenic cases of juvenile cancers. Difficulty stems from the fact that one cannot differentiate between the two sources of cancer and that the contingency tables are truncated. It turns out that the suggested iterative maximum likelihood estimation of parameters has undesirable properties, so that the author uses a minimum modified chi-square approach. Tests of hypothesis are performed, and the following conclusions are drawn: that a radiation hazard exists, that it varies with date of birth, the age distributions of radiogenic versus non-radiogenic cases are different and may exhibit slight changes over time, and that a characteristic latent period can be ascribed to various types of cancers.

The dose-response relationship for radiation carcinogenesis is explored by Rossi and Kellerer (1972), who find that the phenomenon cannot be adequately explained by carcinogenic transformation occurring in individual cells independently of one another. Rosen (1973) demonstrates, theoretically at least, that the phenomenon can be better explained by the addition of an N-contiguous cell effect to the single cell effect.

Albert and Altshuler (1973) consider a lognormal model, credited to Blum (1959) and Druckrey (1967), for time to cancer appearance, that is dose-dependent. Age at occurrence and life-shortening effects are investigated, and the model is shown to fit well to three different sets of cancer data. But recall that Peto, Lee, and

Paige (1972) found the Weibull superior to the lognormal. Special consideration is given to the use of epidemiological data and how the model could be used to determine limits for levels of environmental carcinogens. Here one must consider non-cancer mortality to evaluate life-shortening effects for cancer cases as well as the population as a whole.

C. Cell kinetics

Research into cell kinetics of tumors has been rather more biomathematical than biostatistical in nature, generally with emphasis on implications for tumor therapy. However, contingent on the availability of data, statistical techniques could be applied.

Kuzma et al. (1969) consider a cellular compartment model in which exponential growth is disturbed by chemotherapy. It is assumed that tumor cells may be susceptible to certain drugs only in one phase of growth, whereas for other drugs they are susceptible in all phases (compartments correspond to growth phases). An immediate kill effect and delayed kill effect are considered, and Kuzma et al. determine the theoretical dose level and time pattern to achieve tumor regression. Adjustment is made for different speeds of development in the various phases and for the toxic effect of the treatment. The approach here has certain similarities to that of Neuts (1968) who does not consider a cellular compartment model, but rather a pure birth process disturbed by chemotherapy. He considers effectiveness of treatment and toxicity, as well as maximizing the expected lifetime.

In a highly theoretical model, Mills (1970) describes tumor growth as a diffusion process about an initial site. He indicates the possibility of incorporating magnetic field therapy in the model.

An overview of cell kinetics models is given in Aroesty et al. (1973). They discuss deterministic growth curves as well as a discrete-time stochastic cellular compartment model derived from Kendall (1948) and Takahashi (1966, 1968). For the simplified case of uniform transition rates from one compartment into the next and negligible cell loss, the transit times are gamma-distributed. For the continuous time analogue of this process, Aroesty et al. give the probability distribution for cell cycle time. The point is made that compartmentalization is really arbitrary and that cell growth should be modelled on a continuous scale, in which case solutions to the resultant differential equations are not obtained, and computer simulation is performed. The simulation results indicate that Rubinow's (1968) assumption that generation time is hereditary agrees better with the data of Prescott (1959) than the assumption of no correlation of generation times between parent and offspring. Further, Aroesty et al. discuss response to chemotherapy, with emphasis on recommenced growth between treatments and attainment of equilibrium levels (no further tumor growth), in the presence of chemotherapy, for the Gompertz growth curve. A computer simulation approach is applied to the case of a cellular compartment model under chemotherapeutic response.

Smith and Tuckwell (1974) consider a stochastic version of Gompertzian growth as a model for tumor size. They are able to find analytic expressions for the mean and variance of the logarithm of tumor size, but no comparison is made to experimental data.

Wette et al. (1974 a, b) investigate a stochastic cell kinetics model that assumes tumor growth is a birth and death process in which the death rate is proportional to the volume of the tumor, hence to the number of cells, and the birth rate is proportional to surface area, hence to the number of cells raised to the two-thirds power. This assumption is made because nutrients are presumed sufficient for cell division only on the surface of the tumor. An explicit solution for the probabilities associated with the process is not obtained, but Wette et al. are able to examine asymptotic probability of extinction (equal to one), expected survival time, bounds for the probability of extinction, upper bounds for the mean and variance of tumor size, and bounds for the asymptotic tumor size conditional on the tumor not becoming extinct. The model is revised to account for small tumor size, for which the birth rate should be taken to be proportional to tumor volume (number of cells). As before, an explicit solution is not obtained, but various properties of the model are investigated.

D. Breast cancer

Blumenson and Bross (1969) formulate a model for the growth of breast cancer incorporating the ideas of exponential tumor growth, delay time, involvement of lymph nodes, and probability of recurrence. The probability of detecting a tumor is assumed proportional to the number of times the tumor has doubled its size, and delay time is the difference between the earliest possible time of detection and actual time of detection. The number of lymph nodes affected by the cancer is assumed Poisson-distributed. The probability of metastasis in other parts of the body is taken to be of the same form as delay time, although justification for this assumption is not given. Probabilities are derived for the joint distribution of tumor size, nodal status, and recurrence status. Minimum chi-square estimation is used for the parameters. Blumenson and Bross found the model fit badly to all the studies examined; however, the additional assumption of two different susceptibility subgroups resulted in successful application of chi-square tests.

Alternatively, Tallis and Sarfaty (1974) investigate the probability distribution of delay time in breast cancer with the assumption that the probability of detection is proportional to the rate of tumor growth, and tumor growth is assumed to be exponential. They obtain expression for the expected value of delay time and expected tumor volume at time of reporting, which are applied to some Australian data. However, there is no consideration of goodness of fit of the model.

E. Leukemia

Chow (1972) models the number of leukemic cells as a time-dependent immigration and death process, restricted by the assumption that immigration of leukemic cells into the blood can only take place when their number falls below a certain level. Expressions for probabilities, expectation, and variance are derived (the number of leukemic cells turns out to be the sum of two binomials), in particular for the time-independent case. Limiting properties are investigated. Since the random variable in this model is not observable experimentally, it could not be used to establish goodness of fit. The observable quantity is the density of leukemic cells, and its probability distribution is obtained from the assumption that its conditional distribution, given the total number of leukemic cells, is Poisson. The parameters are estimated by Neyman's modified minimum chi-square method. In a later paper, Chow (1974) uses these results to obtain survival probabilities in a model which assumes the force of mortality is a linear function of non-random concomitant variables and stochastic medical variables, the fluctuation of which affect survival. This is a stochastic elaboration on the work of Feigl and Zelen (1965) and Zippin and Armitage (1966). The probability distribution for a patient's survival is obtained, but in terms of medically unavailable quantities. Two alternative risk functions are applied, the first measuring decreased ability to resist infection (impairment of phagocytization of bacteria) and the second taking into account the additional risk of fatal hemorrhage as well. Two methods of parameter estimation are presented. Note that in neither of Chow's papers is any application to clinical data attempted.

One ought to mention by way of conclusion that, for any model which proves mathematically tractable, a goodness-of-fit comparison to data can be made via simulation studies. Such a procedure, although not applied to carcinogenesis, is delineated in Hoel and Mitchell (1971) and could be used with cancer models. There are also a number of non-statistical models for carcinogenesis, for example, Blair (1968) and Janson and Revesz (1974), that could lend themselves to statistical analysis in the future.

3. Immunological Response as a Factor in Carcinogenesis

The above models lack any explicit consideration of immunological feedback built into the underlying assumptions. Nevertheless, the phenomenon of immunological response is important in the cancer problem. Burnet (1964) provides a review of immunological factors in carcinogenesis. Weiss (1967) maintains that studies of neoplastic diseases in both humans and animals indicate that the host tissue does not play an entirely passive role in the progress of the disease. His work on mammary tumors in mice demonstrated the existence of an immunological response by the host tissue against the tumor, i.e., the tumor produces antigens against which the normal tissue reacts. Further, in his 1969 paper Weiss reports that with few, if any, exceptions, all animal tumors thus far subjected to systematic investigation have exhibited immunological feedback. Also, Iverson (1965) stresses the need to take into account a feedback mechanism in a biocybernetic approach to cancer. Clearly, it is appropriate to include immunological response in a mathematical model for carcinogenesis.

Weiss (1967) notes the seeming discrepancy between the fact of tumor antigenicity and the fact that malignant tumors, once detectable, commonly grow until the death of the host. It is here that a probabilistic viewpoint helps. If, at a given time, there is some probability of the death of a cancer cell due to an immunological response, in addition to a non-immunological death probability, then there will be some probability that a tumor "escapes" the immunological response. If so, the tumor will grow until the death of the host. Further, these probability arguments can be used to explain the phenomena of remission and exacerbation in tumor growth. During remission the tumor is subject to immunological response and during the period of exacerbation the tumor "escapes" that response. These probabilistic ideas, albeit simplistic, may serve to elucidate the paradox.

Immunological feedback may also explain the hypercellularity observed by Shimkin and Polissar, which led to the postulation of a two-stage hypothesis. Recall that Shimkin considers two possiblities, that the hyperplastic foci are independent of the tumors or that the hyperplastic foci are precursors to the tumors, composed of cells which have a probability of mutating into cancer cells. But there is a third possibility: merely that the hyperplastic foci are composed of cancer cells and that the observed hypercellularity is an expression of immunological response against the incipient tumors. Those tumors that develop would be those that escape the effect of immunoligical feedback. The consequences of that assumption, as an alternative to the two-stage model, constitute the goal of this investigation. Thus, we hypothesize a one-stage model with immunological feedback.

4. The Mathematical Model

Let $X(t)$ be the number of tumor cells at time t, and $\Pr\{X(t) = n\} = p_n(t)$ is

the density of X. A "birth", i.e., an increase of one of the total population of

cancer cells, can occur either by mutation of a normal cell caused by the action

of the carcinogen, consisting of randomly (Poisson) distributed hits, or by repro-

duction of existing cancer cells. A death of a tumor cell occurs as an additive

combination of non-immunological and immunological elements. Once a tumor is

initiated by carcinogenic action, it undergoes a birth and death process with

infinitesimal birth rate linear and infinitesimal death rate composed of a linear

and a nonlinear term, the former due to non-immunological deaths, the latter to

immunological feedback. The death rate per tumor cell due to immunological response

is proportional to the total number of antigen-producing (tumor) cells; thus, the

total death rate is quadratic. Although this assumes a very simple mechanism for

the action of immunological feedback, it is nevertheless a first step.

Summarizing, we have

$\Pr\{\Delta X(t)=+1,$ due to mutation$|X(t)=n\} = D(t)\Delta t+0(\Delta t)$

$\Pr\{\Delta X(t)=+1,$ due to reproduction$|X(t)=n\} = \lambda n\Delta t+0(\Delta t)$

(1) $\Pr\{\Delta X(t)=-1,$ due to non-immunological deaths$|X(t) = \mu n\Delta t+0(\Delta t)$

$\Pr\{\Delta X(t)=-1,$ due to to immunological response$|X(t)=n\} = \kappa n^2\Delta t+0(\Delta t)$

$\Pr\{\Delta X(t)=0|X(t)=n\} = 1 - [D(t)+\lambda n+\mu n+\kappa n^2]\Delta t + 0(\Delta t)$

as $\Delta t \rightarrow 0$, with initial condition X = 0 at t = 0 with probability one. Here λ,μ,κ

> 0, $\lambda-\mu > \kappa$ [see discussion following (15)], $D(t) \geq 0$ for all t, and $0(\Delta t)/\Delta t \rightarrow 0$

as $\Delta t \rightarrow 0$. Note that only transitions of ±1 are allowed in small Δt. $D(t)$ is a

function of time relating to the dosage of carcinogen.

In order to elucidate the difference between the feedback and the non-feedback

model, we examine the graphs for the transition probabilities of births and deaths.

Supposing D = D(t) is a constant, we compare D + λn and μn vs. n (for the non-

feedback model) and D + λn and μn + κn² vs. n (for the feedback model) in Figs. 1

and 2 with X substituted for n. There we see that for the non-feedback case the

difference of the birth minus the death probability is increasing linearly with n.

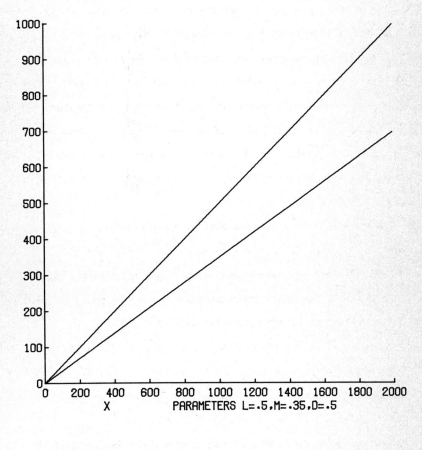

D+LAMBDA*X   AND   MU*X   VERSUS   X

X   VERSUS X1   200 VALUES $x1 = D + \lambda_{.}X$
X   VERSUS X2   200 VALUES $x2 = \mu_{.}X$

FIGURE 1

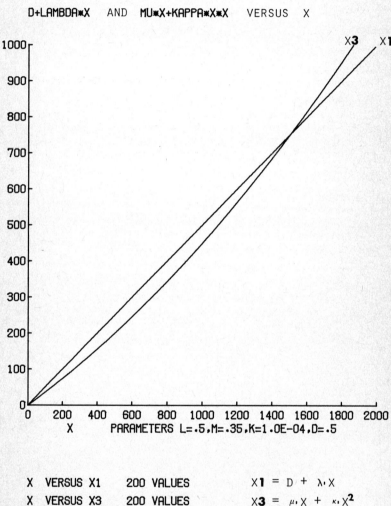

FIGURE **2**

This would not be in agreement with the observed hypercellularity of tumor cells. In the case where immunological feedback is included, the same difference in transition probabilities decreases to zero at the point $n = (\lambda-\mu)/\kappa$ and then deaths outstrip births in probability. Nevertheless, there is still a positive probability that a tumor will become large. The above appears more consistent with the observed phenomena in tumor development.

The above defined transition probabilities describe a stochastic process known in the literature as a nonlinear birth and death process with immigration. From this point we shall focus on the nonlinear birth and death process generated by a single tumor cell, given that its initiation by the carcinogenic agent has already taken place. We are abandoning the more complicated collective process for the present. We consider a stochastic process with infinitesimal transition probabilities

$$\Pr\{\Delta X(t)= +1 \mid X(t) = n\} = \lambda n \Delta t + O(\Delta t)$$

$$\Pr\{\Delta X(t)= -1 \mid X(t) = n\} = (\mu n + \kappa n^2)\Delta t + O(\Delta t)$$

$$\Pr\{\Delta X(t) = 0 \mid X(t) = n\} = 1 - (\lambda n + \mu n + \kappa n^2)\Delta t + O(\Delta t)$$

as $t \to 0$,

where we have let $D = 0$ and now have initial condition $X(0) = 1$ with probability one. The forward Kolmogorov difference equations (see Karlin, 1969, p. 193) are obtained:

$$\frac{dp_n(t)}{dt} = \lambda(n-1)p_{n-1}(t) - (\lambda+\mu+\kappa n)np_n(t) + [\mu+\kappa(n+1)](n+1)p_{n+1}(t),$$

(3) $(n \geq 1)$

$$\frac{dp_0(t)}{dt} = (\mu+\kappa)p_1(t).$$

A unique solution for these equations is guaranteed, since

$$\sum_{n=1}^{\infty} \frac{1}{\lambda n} = \frac{1}{\lambda} \sum_{n=1}^{\infty} \frac{1}{n}$$

is divergent (Bailey, 1964, pp. 101-102, and Bharucha-Reid, 1960, p. 91 et seq.). For the probability generating function,

$$P(z,t) = \sum_{n=0}^{\infty} p_n(t)z^n,$$

we have

(4) $\dfrac{\partial P(z,t)}{\partial t} = \lambda(z^2-z)\dfrac{\partial P}{\partial z} + (\mu+\kappa)(1-z)\dfrac{\partial P}{\partial z} + \kappa(z-z^2)\dfrac{\partial^2 P}{\partial z^2}$.

If we could solve either the difference equation for the density or the partial differential equation for the probability generating function, the process would be completely described.

The standard approach to equations such as (4) is separation of variables. Let

$$P(z,t) = m(z)n(t).$$

This gives the separated equations

(5) $\dfrac{n'(t)}{n(t)} = \text{constant},$

$$\dfrac{[\lambda(z^2-z) + (\mu+\kappa)(1-z)]m'(z) + \kappa(z-z^2)m''(z)}{m(z)} = \text{constant}.$$

The first is easily solved to yield

(6) $n(t) = e^{-c_1 t}$,

where c_1 is a constant to be determined from the initial conditions. The second can be written

(7) $\kappa(z-z^2)m''(z) + [\lambda(z^2-z) + (\mu+\kappa)(1-z)]m'(z) + c_1 m(z) = 0$

for which we attempt a power series solution. Let $m(z) = \sum_{n=0}^{\infty} a_n z^n$

Direct substitution yields

$$\kappa(z-z^2) \sum_{n=0}^{\infty} a_n n(n-1)z^{n-2} + [\lambda(z^2-z)+(\mu+\kappa)(1-z)] \sum_{n=0}^{\infty} a_n n z^{n-1} + c_1 \sum_{n=0}^{\infty} a_n z^n = 0.$$

After some manipulation we have

$$\sum_{n=2}^{\infty} \lambda(n-2)a_{n-2}z^{n-1} + \sum_{n=1}^{\infty} [-\kappa(n-1)^2-(\lambda+\mu)(n-1)+c_1]a_{n-1}z^{n-1}$$

$$+ \sum_{n=0}^{\infty} (\kappa n^2+\mu n)a_n x^{n-1} = 0.$$

This leads to the following many-term recurrence relation which, in general, cannot be solved analytically:

$$(n\mu + n^2\kappa)a_n - [(n-1)(\lambda+\mu) + (n-1)^2\kappa - c_1]a_{n-1} + \lambda(n-2)a_{n-2} = 0,$$

(8)

$$n \geq 3.$$

So we try another method. We apply the Laplace transform

(9) $\quad q_n(s) = \int_e^{\infty} e^{-st}p_n(t)dt$

to the differential-difference equations (3).

$$sq_n = \lambda(n-1)q_{n-1}-(\lambda+\mu+\kappa n)nq_n+[\mu+\kappa(n+1)](n+1)q_{n+1} \qquad (n > 1)$$

(10) $\quad sq_1 - 1 = -(\lambda+\mu+\kappa)q_1 + (\mu+2\kappa)2q_2$

$$sq_0 = (\mu+\kappa)q_1$$

Bailey (1963, 1964) is able for the simple stochastic epidemic to use this method to obtain a solution for q_n since in his case the equation for q_0 does not depend upon q_1. However, that approach does not apply here.

Next we attempt to get information from the differential equations for the moments. For the moment generating function,

$$M(\theta,t) = \sum_{j=0}^{\infty} p_j(t)e^{\theta j}$$

we have

(11) $\quad \dfrac{\partial M}{\partial t} = [\lambda(e^{\theta}-1) + \mu(e^{-\theta}-1)]\dfrac{\partial M}{\partial \theta} + \kappa(e^{-\theta}-1)\dfrac{\partial^2 M}{\partial \theta^2}$

Consider the Taylor series expansion of $M(\theta,t)$ about the origin

$$M(\theta,t) = 1 + \sum_{r=1}^{\infty} \mu_r(t)\frac{\theta^r}{r!}$$

where $\mu_r(t) = \dfrac{\partial^r}{\partial \theta^r} M(\theta,t)\big|_{\theta=0}$

Then

$$\frac{\partial M}{\partial t} = \sum_{r=1}^{\infty} \frac{\partial \mu_r}{\partial t} \frac{\theta^r}{r!} \quad ,$$

$$\frac{\partial M}{\partial \theta} = \sum_{r=1}^{\infty} \mu_r \frac{\theta^{r-1}}{(r-1)!}$$

$$\frac{\partial^2 M}{\partial \theta^2} = \sum_{r=2}^{\infty} \mu_r \frac{\theta^{r-2}}{(r-2)!}$$

Equating coefficients of θ in (11) gives

$$\frac{d\mu_1}{dt} = (\lambda-\mu)\mu_1 - \kappa\mu_2$$

(12) $\quad \dfrac{1}{2} \cdot \dfrac{d\mu_2}{dt} = \dfrac{(\lambda+\mu)}{2}\mu_1 + (\lambda-\mu)\mu_2 - \kappa\mu_3 + \kappa\mu_2 \qquad\qquad$ (r=2)

$\quad \dfrac{1}{6} \cdot \dfrac{d\mu_3}{dt} = \dfrac{(\lambda-\mu)}{6}\mu_1 + \dfrac{(\lambda+\mu)}{4}\mu_2 + \dfrac{(\lambda-\mu)}{2}\mu_3 - \kappa\mu_2 + \kappa\mu_3 - \dfrac{\kappa}{2}\mu_4 \qquad$ (r=3)

etc.

In general, the ith equation, for $\dfrac{d\mu_i}{dt}$, contains μ_{i+1}, otherwise we could obtain a solution for $\mu_1,\ldots,\mu_i$ at least theoretically. Thus, this method proves abortive, too.

That our equations should prove intractable is not surprising since Kendall (1949) found the same in dealing with the logistic process of which our process is a special case. It should be pointed out, however, that the equations for certain nonlinear birth and death processes have been solved. See Barlett (1955) for the general birth process, John (1961) for the quadratic birth process, Bailey

(1963, 1964) for the simple stochastic epidemic, Severo (1967, 1969), Gani (1965)

and Siskind (1965) for the general stochastic epidemic, Dietz (1966) for the carrier-

borne epidemic, Billard (1974) for a competition model with deaths (or births)

only allowed, Moran (1958) and Bather (1963) for a genetic model with balanced

nonlinearities, and Bather (ibid.) for a process with linear eigen-values. Efforts

to apply the methods used in the above references were not successful for the

present model. Lack of boundedness is a problem, as well as the fact that both

births and deaths are possible.

Despite the fact that an exact solution for the density or generating functions

is not obtained, certain properties of process can be derived. We can write the

differential equation for the deterministic formulation of the model as

(13) $\quad \frac{dx}{dt} = \lambda x - (\mu+\kappa x)x, \quad x = 1 \text{ at } t = 0,$

where x is the number of tumor cells. This is a special case of logistic growth

(Pielou, 1969); hence

(14) $\quad x(t) = \dfrac{(\lambda-\mu)}{(\lambda-\mu-\kappa)e^{-(\kappa-\mu)t}+\kappa}$

(see Fig. 3). The implications of this are that a tumor grows to an asymptotic

upper limit given by

(15) $\quad \lim_{t\to\infty} x(t) = \frac{\lambda-\mu}{\kappa} \quad .$

Since we expect the maximum tumor size to be large, i.e. contain many cells,

we have

$$(\lambda-\mu) \gg \kappa.$$

In the deterministic formulation, the tumor cannot exceed its asymptotic upper

limit because of maximum size limitations. This, however, is not the case in

a stochastic formulation.

Returning to the stochastic model, note that with the single absorbing barrier

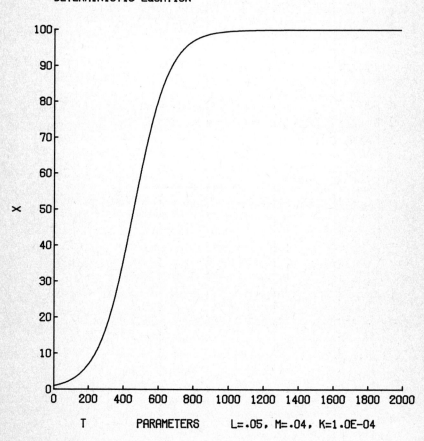

DETERMINISTIC EQUATION

T   PARAMETERS   L=.05, M=.04, K=1.0E-04

T VERSUS X   200 VALUES

FIGURE **3a**

DETERMINISTIC EQUATION

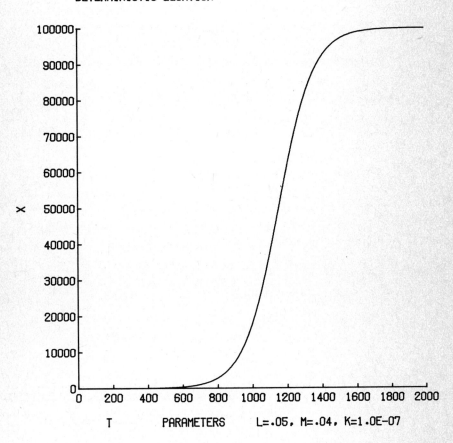

T   PARAMETERS   L=.05, M=.04, K=1.0E-07

T VERSUS X   200 VALUES

FIGURE **3b**

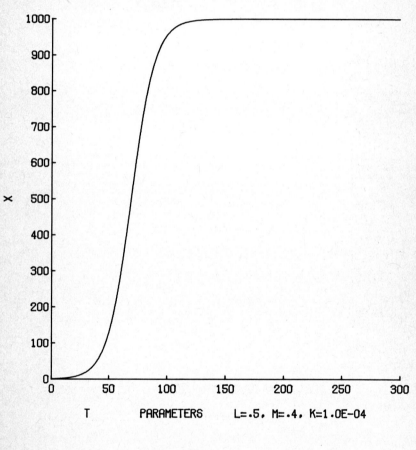

DETERMINISTIC EQUATION

T   PARAMETERS   L=.5, M=.4, K=1.0E-04

T VERSUS X   300 VALUES

FIGURE **3c**

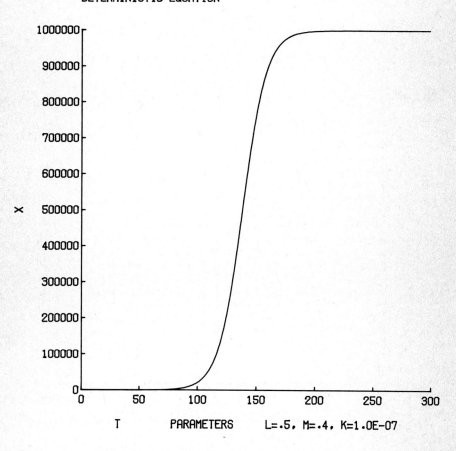

DETERMINISTIC EQUATION

T   PARAMETERS   L=.5, M=.4, K=1.0E-07

T   VERSUS X   300 VALUES

FIGURE **3d**

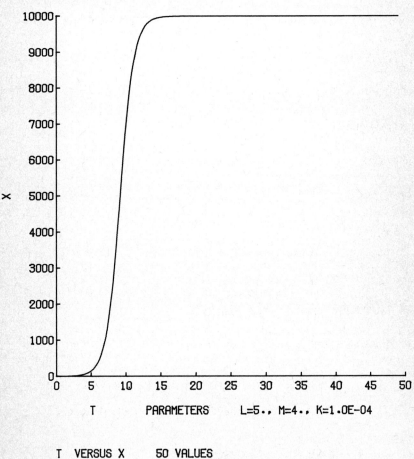

DETERMINISTIC EQUATION

T VERSUS X   50 VALUES

FIGURE **3e**

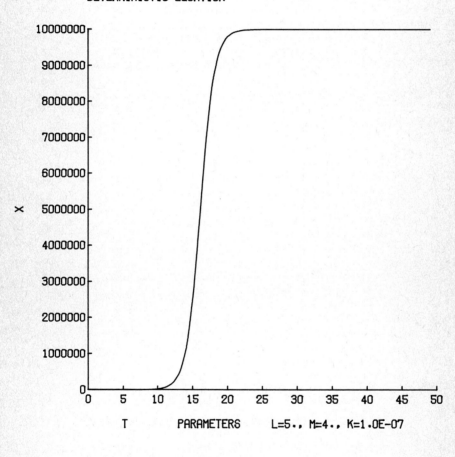

DETERMINISTIC EQUATION

T   PARAMETERS   L=5., M=4., K=1.0E-07

T VERSUS X   50 VALUES

FIGURE **3f**

at x = 0 (corresponding to the extinction of the tumor colony), the only stationary distribution of the process is degenerate with unit mass at X = 0 [confirmed by (19)]. Thus we know

(16) $\lim_{t \to \infty} P(z,t) = 1$

Note also that the process satisfies the boundary condition X = 1 at t = 0, with probability one. This means

(17) $P(z,0) = z.$

Karlin (1969, p. 205) gives the probability of absorption into state X = 0, where for our case Karlin's notation becomes $\lambda_j = \lambda \cdot j$, $\mu_j = \mu \cdot j + \kappa j^2$, as

$$\lim_{t \to \infty} \Pr[X(t) = 0 | X(0) = 1]$$

(18)
$$= \frac{\sum\limits_{i=1}^{\infty} \left[\prod\limits_{j=1}^{i} \frac{\mu_j}{\lambda_j} \right]}{1 + \sum\limits_{i=1}^{\infty} \left[\prod\limits_{j=1}^{i} \frac{\mu_j}{\lambda_j} \right]}$$

$$= \frac{\sum\limits_{i=1}^{\infty} \left[\prod\limits_{j=1}^{i} \frac{(\mu + \kappa \cdot j)}{\lambda} \right]}{1 + \sum\limits_{i=1}^{\infty} \left[\prod\limits_{j=1}^{i} \frac{(\mu + \kappa \cdot j)}{\lambda} \right]}$$

We can write

$$S = \sum_{i=1}^{\infty} \left[\prod_{j=1}^{i} \frac{(\mu + \kappa \cdot j)}{\lambda} \right]$$

$$= \sum_{i=1}^{[\frac{\lambda - \mu}{\kappa}]} \left[\prod_{j=1}^{i} \frac{(\mu + \kappa \cdot j)}{\lambda} \right] + \sum_{i=[\frac{\lambda - \mu}{\kappa}]+1}^{\infty} \left[\prod_{j=1}^{i} \frac{(\mu + \kappa \cdot j)}{\lambda} \right]$$

where [ ] means, "the greatest integer less than or equal to". But

$$W = \sum_{i=[\frac{\lambda-\mu}{\kappa}]+1}^{\infty} \left(\prod_{j=1}^{i} \frac{(\mu+\kappa \cdot j)}{\lambda} \right)$$

$$= \prod_{j=1}^{[\frac{\lambda-\mu}{\kappa}]} \left(\frac{\mu+\kappa \cdot j}{\lambda} \right) \sum_{i=[\frac{\lambda-\mu}{\kappa}]+1}^{\infty} \left(\prod_{j=[\frac{\lambda-\mu}{\kappa}]+1}^{i} \frac{(\mu+\kappa \cdot j)}{\lambda} \right) \quad .$$

For $j \geq \frac{\lambda-\mu}{\kappa}$, $\frac{\mu+\kappa \cdot j}{\lambda} \geq 1$, so that

$$\prod_{j=[\frac{\lambda-\mu}{\kappa}]+1}^{i} \left(\frac{\mu+\kappa \cdot j}{\lambda} \right) \geq 1 \text{ for } i \geq j,$$

and so $\sum_{i=[\frac{\lambda-\mu}{\kappa}]+1}^{\infty} \left(\prod_{j=[\frac{\lambda-\mu}{\kappa}]+1}^{\infty} \frac{(\mu+\kappa \cdot j)}{\lambda} \right)$ diverges.

Therefore W, hence S, diverges, which means

(19) $\lim_{t \to \infty} \Pr[X(t) = 0 | X(0) = 1] = 1.$

Since an analytic solution for neither the probability generating function nor the density is obtained, it will be useful to recall the above properties once we have derived approximations to the process.

The question arises as to whether it might not be preferable to attempt a numerical solution for the state probabilities, $p_n(t)$, as opposed to an approximate analytic solution for these probabilities. Recall that the stochastic process (i.e. tumor size) is unbounded, hence we would have to find an infinite number of state probabilities at each point in time for which we attempt a numerical solution. Even if we take a conservative bound of, say, 10^6 for the number of cells in a tumor [Weiss (1967), for example, uses tumor implants of order 10^5 in mice], ignoring the possibility of a larger tumor or else considering the maximum size as an absorbing barrier, finding individual state probabilities would be prohibitive in computer time and money. At each point in time for which we require a set of state probabilities, we must find one million such probabilities. Clearly then, the only "maximum" tumor sizes for which a numerical solution would be feasible (even an 1000 x 100 array would be outsized for a large computer), would be grossly unrealistic biologically.

5. Some Unsuccessful Approaches to the Approximation Problem

Although, as the heading indicates, the methods in this chapter do not yield useful results for the stochastic process we seek to approximate here, they provide insight into the difficulties of approximating nonlinear birth and death processes in general. That these methods fail for the nonlinear process at hand is no indication that they would not yield useful results for others.

A. Continuous Approximations

Under this heading will be presented a group of approximation techniques, suggested by Bailey (1964), which share the following features:

(i) $p_n(t)$, which is discrete, is replaced by $p(x,t)$, a continuous density, so that the forward Kolmogorov equation (3) becomes

$$(20) \qquad \frac{\partial p(x,t)}{\partial t} = \lambda(x-1)p(x-1,t) - (\lambda+\mu+\kappa x)xp(x,t)$$
$$+[\mu+\kappa(x+1)](x+1)p(x+1,t),$$

(ii) x is assumed to be large enough so that $x \approx x-1$ and $x \approx x+1$,

(iii) Taylor series expansion for $p(x,t)$ are used retaining first order terms only,

$$p(x-1,t) = p(x,t) - \frac{\partial p}{\partial x}$$
$$(21)$$
$$p(x+1,t) = p(x,t) + \frac{\partial p}{\partial x} .$$

1) Using the density, $p(x,t)$.

Applying assumption (ii) to assumption (i), we have

$$(22) \qquad \frac{\partial p}{\partial t} \approx \lambda x[p(x-1,t) - p(x,t)] + (\mu+\kappa x)x[p(x+1,t) - p(x,t)].$$

Applying (iii) yields

$$(23) \qquad \frac{\partial p}{\partial t} = [(\mu+\kappa x)x - \lambda x]\frac{\partial p}{\partial x} .$$

The solution can be obtained (Dubin, 1974, pp. 25-27) as

$$(24) \quad p(x,t) = \frac{x(\lambda-\mu-\kappa)}{|\lambda-\mu-\kappa x|} e^{-(\lambda-\mu)t} , \quad x \neq 0, \frac{\lambda-\mu}{\kappa} .$$

Note that it is assumed implicitly that x, the number of tumor cells, takes on non-negative values only.

The assumption that $x \neq 0$ for our approximation is a difficulty. After all, we would want to be able to calculate the probability of extinction, $p(0,t)$, but here we cannot. Further,

$$\lim_{x \to \frac{\lambda-\mu}{\kappa} \pm} p(x,t) = + \infty ,$$

which in a general sense suggests a concentration of probability around the deterministic carrying capacity, $(\lambda - \mu)/\kappa$. But $p(x,t)$ is non-integrable and not summable in Cesaro mean (Dubin, 1974 pp. 27-29), which is highly undesirable since we require, for $p(x,t)$ to be a probability distribution, that

$$\int_x p(x,t)dx = 1.$$

We can attempt an improvement to this approximate density by expanding to second order terms in the Taylor series in assumption (iii), but this is no more successful than the first order approximation (Dubin, ibid.).

2) Using log $p(x,t)$.

Bailey (1964, pp. 208-209) finds that effecting the transformation

$$(25) \quad \ell(x,t) = \log p(x,t)$$

yields better results than attempting a solution with method A for $p(x,t)$ itself. Applying (25) to assumption (i) gives

$$\frac{\partial \ell(x,t)}{\partial t} = e^{-\ell(x,t)}\{\lambda(x-1)e^{\ell(x-1,t)} - (\lambda+\mu+\kappa x)xc^{\ell(x,t)}$$
$$+ [\mu+\kappa(x+1)](x+1)e^{\ell(x+1,t)}\}.$$

Using assumption (ii) and the Taylor series approximation in (iii) with ℓ

substituted for p yields, analogously to method A,

(26) $\quad \dfrac{\partial \ell}{\ell t} \approx \lambda x e^{-\partial \ell / \partial x} - (\lambda + \mu + \kappa x) x + (\mu + \kappa x) x e^{\partial \ell / \partial x}$.

Let $\partial \ell / \partial t = a$, $\phi = \exp(\partial \ell / \partial x)$. Then

$$\lambda x \phi^{-1} + (\mu + \kappa x) x \phi = a + \lambda x + \mu x + \kappa x^2,$$

which has the solutions

(27) $\quad \phi = \dfrac{a + (\lambda + \mu + \kappa x) x \pm d}{2 (\mu + \kappa x) x},$

where $d = [\{a + (\lambda + \mu + \kappa x) x\}^2 - 4(\mu + \kappa x) \lambda x^2]^{\frac{1}{2}}$.

Taking the logarithm of both sides, we have

(28) $\quad \dfrac{\partial \ell}{\partial x} = \log[a + (\lambda + \mu + \kappa x) x \pm d] - \log[2(\mu + \kappa x) x]$.

We set aside for now the difficulties generated by the existence of two distinct solutions. The quadratic nature arises not, as might be expected, because of the quadratic term in the transition probability for deaths, but because both birth and deaths are allowed in the model. If we could integrate (28), we would have two answers, but because of the complicated nature of "d" such integration proved beyond the capabilities of the author and standard tables. As a result several further approximations were tried, but proved abortive (Dubin, 1974 pp. 32-36).

   3) Laplace transform approach.

       The motivation for this method is the awkwardness of incorporating initial conditions in an approximate solution. By using the Laplace transform with respect to time, initial conditions are included in the basic difference equation. Bailey suggests using the transform in combination with the previous logarithm approach. We apply

$$q(x,s) = \int_0^\infty e^{-st} p(x,t) dt$$

to equation (20) to obtain the continuous analogue of (10),

$$sq(x,s) = \lambda(x-1)q(x-1,s) - (\lambda+\mu+\kappa x)xq(x,s) + [\mu+\kappa(x+1)](x+1)q(x+1,s), \quad x > 1$$

(29) $$sq(1,s) - 1 = -(\lambda+\mu+\kappa)q(1,s) + 2(\mu+2\kappa)q(2,s),$$

$$sq(0,s) = (\mu+\kappa)q(1,s).$$

The result obtained is

(30) $$q(x,s) = \frac{\lambda^{(x-1)}(\mu+\kappa)^{(\frac{\mu}{\kappa} + 1)}e^{(x-1)}}{(\mu+\kappa x)^{(x+\mu/\kappa)}[s-\lambda+\mu+\kappa - \frac{2\lambda\kappa}{(\mu+\kappa)}]}$$

The derivation can be found in Dubin (1974, pp. 37-39).

Taking the inverse transform yields

(31) $$p(x,t) = \frac{\lambda^{(x-1)}(\mu+\kappa)^{(1+\frac{\mu}{\kappa})}e^{(x-1)}}{(\mu+\kappa x)^{(x+\frac{\mu}{\kappa})}} \exp[\{\frac{2\lambda\kappa}{(\mu+\kappa)} +\lambda-\mu-\kappa\}t].$$

Examination of this density reveals that, since

$$\frac{2\lambda\kappa}{(\mu+\kappa)} > 0, \qquad \lambda > \mu + \kappa$$

we have

$$\lim_{t\to\infty} p(x,t) = +\infty.$$

This is unacceptable. Details of the derivation can be found in Dubin (1974, pp. 37-41), as well as another attempt to use Laplace transforms which resorts unsuccessfully to a saddle point approximation.

It does not appear that we have obtained any useful approximations from these continuous approximation techniques. This is radically different from what Bailey (1964) found. In his examination of the Poisson process and the birth process, two stochastic processes for which the exact solution is available, the continuous approximation methods gave quite good results. Perhaps this can be explained by the simplicity of the processes considered by Bailey; in the nonlinear case studied at the present, the continuous approximations do not work well at all.

B. Neglect of Higher-Order Cumulants

Suppose we consider the cumulant generating function, $C(\theta,t) = \log[M(\theta,t)]$.

Differentiation and substitution in (11) gives

(32) $\quad \frac{\partial C}{\partial t} = [\lambda(e^\theta - 1) + \mu(e^{-\theta} - 1)]\frac{\partial C}{\partial \theta} + \kappa(e^{-\theta} - 1)[\frac{\partial^2 C}{\partial \theta^2} + (\frac{\partial C}{\partial \theta})^2]$.

Using the Taylor series technique following equation (11) one obtains the sequence

of equations

$$\frac{dc_1}{dt} = (\lambda - \mu)c_1 - \kappa(c_2 + c_1^2)$$

(33) $\quad \frac{1}{2} \cdot \frac{dc_2}{dt} = (\lambda - \mu)c_2 + \frac{1}{2}(\lambda + \mu)c_1 - \kappa(c_3 + 2c_1 c_2) + \frac{\kappa}{2}(c_2 + c_1^2)$,

.
.
.

etc.

where $C = \sum\limits_{i=1}^{\infty} c_i(t)\frac{\theta^i}{i!}$. In general the ith equation, for $\frac{dc_i}{dt}$, contains c_{i+1}, other-

wise we could obtain a solution for $c_1, \ldots, c_i$. This is analogous to what we found

earlier for the moments.

Whittle (1957) and Bailey (1964) have both suggested neglecting cumulants of

order higher than two. Whittle feels that the approximation is natural; after all,

the assumption that cumulants higher than order one are zero leads to a determin-

istic formulation for the model. Allowing second order cumulants can then be

considered a refinement of that first step. Clearly the resulting stochastic

process will be Gaussian, the normal distribution being the unique distribution

with only first and second cumulants non-zero. The actual physical or mathematical

justification for neglect of cumulants is not apparent, but Whittle refers to good

results of Chandrasekhar (1955) in an application of the theory of turbulence.

The cumulants can be expressed in terms of the moments as

$$c_1 = \mu_1,$$

$$c_2 = \mu_2 - \mu_1^2,$$

(34)
$$c_3 = \mu_3 - 3\mu_1\mu_2 + 2\mu_1^3,$$

.

.

.

etc.

When we neglect the third cumulant, we are assuming that

$$\mu_3 - 3\mu_1\mu_2 + 2\mu_1^3 = 0.$$

Likewise there will be a corresponding assumption for each consecutive cumulant. Under this set of assumptions, (33) becomes

(35)
$$\frac{dc_1}{dt} = (\lambda-\mu)c_1 - \kappa c_2 - \kappa c_1^2,$$

$$\frac{dc_2}{dt} = (2\lambda-2\mu+\kappa)c_2 + (\lambda+\mu)c_1 - 4\kappa c_1 c_2 + \kappa c_1^2.$$

Rearranging, the first equation of (35) becomes

(36)
$$c_2 = \frac{\lambda - \mu}{\kappa} c_1 - c_1^2 - \frac{1}{\kappa} \frac{dc_1}{dt}.$$

and taking derivatives,

(37)
$$\frac{dc_2}{dt} = \frac{\lambda - \mu}{\kappa} \frac{dc_1}{dt} - 2c_1 \frac{dc_1}{dt} - \frac{1}{\kappa} \frac{d^2c_1}{dt^2}.$$

The second equation of (35) together with (37) gives the second-order equation,

(38)
$$\frac{d^2c_1}{dt^2} + [6\kappa c_1 - 3(\lambda-\mu)-\kappa]\frac{dc_1}{dt} + 4\kappa^2 c_1^3 + 6\kappa(\mu-\kappa)c_1^2 + 2[(\lambda-\mu)^2 + \kappa\lambda]c_1 = 0.$$

An exact solution to the above equation was not found; however, a perturbation approximation is derived in Dubin (1974, Appendix II). This approximation technique approaches the exact solution as $\kappa \to 0$ (Cunningham, 1958). Since for our model κ is very small, we expect this approximation to work well. From Dubin (ibid.) we have

$$(39) \quad c_1(t) = \sum_{i=1}^{4} a_i e^{i(\lambda-\mu)t} + \sum_{i=1}^{2} b_i te^{i(\lambda-\mu)t}$$

where the a_i and b_i are functions of λ, μ, and κ.

Once we have an approximation for c_1, we can obtain an expression for c_2 from the relation (36). We give the result only, the details can be found in Dubin (ibid.). It is

$$(40) \quad c_2(t) = \sum_{i=1}^{6} d_i e^{i(\lambda-\mu)t} + \sum_{i=2}^{4} f_i te^{i(\lambda-\mu)t}$$

where the d_i and f_i are functions of λ, μ, and κ.

The moment generating function can be written as

$$(41) \quad M(\theta,t) = \exp[c_1(t)\theta + c_2(t)\frac{\theta^2}{2}] \, ,$$

and the density

$$(42) \quad p(x,t) = \frac{1}{\sqrt{2\pi c_2(t)}} \exp[- \frac{\{x - c_1(t)\}^2}{2c_2(t)}].$$

This approximation method has the advantage over the previous methods in that at least we derive a stochastic process that has a proper probability distribution over time. Unfortunately, this approximation is continuous, whereas the exact model is discrete. Recall also that (39) and (40) are approximations to an approximation since, in addition to assuming cumulants of order higher than two negligible, it was necessary to apply a perturbation approximation. These are all drawbacks, and in total we have no insight into the change of the nature of the stochastic process that has been effected. Analysis of the result is not encouraging. We have

$$\lim_{t\to\infty} c_1(t) = -\infty,$$

$$(43) \quad \lim_{t\to\infty} c_2(t) = -\infty,$$

$$\lim_{t\to\infty} M(\theta,t) = 0.$$

The first of these follows because a_4, the coefficient of its leading term as $t \to \infty$, is negative. The second and third derive from similar reasoning for d_6. Since our original stochastic process is non-negative, an asymptotic mean at negative infinity does not recommend the cumulant method. In any case a negative stochastic variance is absurd. Finally, the last equation in (43) contradicts the known stationary distribution of the exact process,

$$\lim_{t \to \infty} M(\theta,t) = 1,$$

namely, unit mass at $X = 0$. Convergence in Cesaro mean for either the mean c_1 or the variance c_2 depends on the behavior of the leading term $e^{i(\lambda-\mu)t}$ where $i = 4$ for the former and $i = 6$ for the latter. In either case

$$\lim_{c \to \infty} \frac{1}{c} \cdot \sum_{t=0}^{c-1} e^{i(\lambda-\mu)t} \geq \lim_{c \to \infty} \frac{i(\lambda-\mu)}{c} \sum_{t=0}^{c-1} t = \lim_{c \to \infty} i(\lambda-\mu) \cdot \frac{(c-1)}{2} = +\infty$$

Figures 4 and 5 show plots of c_1 and c_2 for the cumulant method. All the factors above, taken with the heavy algebra required to obtain the approximation, lead to the conclusion that some other approximation technique needs to be found.

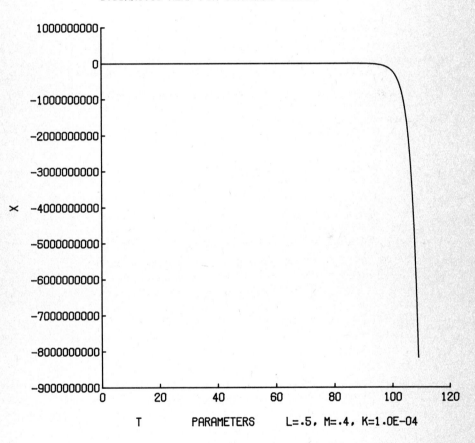

STOCHASTIC MEAN FOR CUMULANT METHOD

FIGURE **4a**

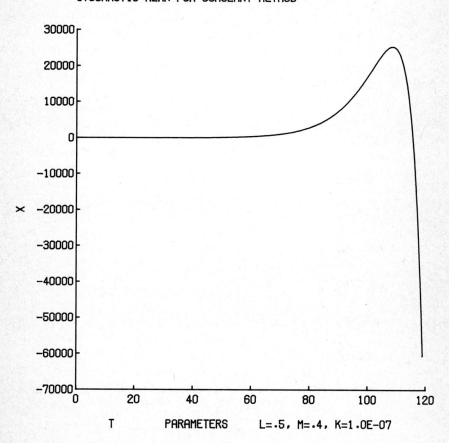

STOCHASTIC MEAN FOR CUMULANT METHOD

T   PARAMETERS   L=.5, M=.4, K=1.0E-07

T   VERSUS X2   120 VALUES

FIGURE **4b**

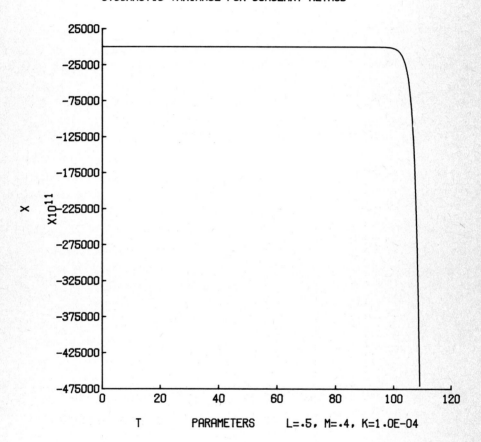

STOCHASTIC VARIANCE FOR CUMULANT METHOD

T   PARAMETERS   L=.5, M=.4, K=1.0E-04

T   VERSUS X2   110 VALUES

FIGURE 5a

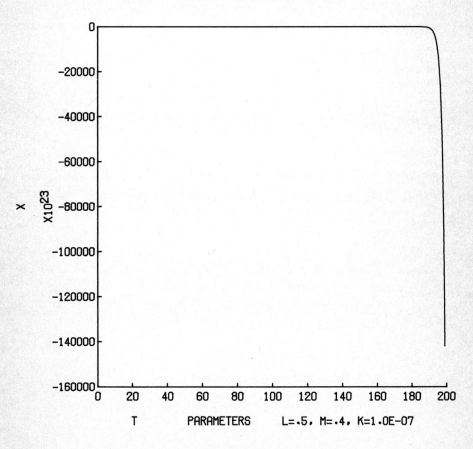

STOCHASTIC VARIANCE FOR CUMULANT METHOD

T   PARAMETERS   L=.5, M=.4, K=1.0E-07

T   VERSUS X2   200 VALUES

FIGURE **5b**

6.   Stochastic Linearization

Here we consider small fluctuations about an equilibrium point. The object
is to obtain the mean and variance of those stochastic fluctuations, rather than
a stochastic process which approximates our exact model. A discussion of stochastic
linearization is considered here because it bears a relation to van Kampen's
approximation method, which follows it. Stochastic linearization was first
presented in detail by Bartlett et al. (1960), but can be found in somewhat more
comprehensible form in Pielou (1969).

The deterministic formulation of our model can be written

$$(44) \quad dX = (\lambda X - \mu X - \kappa X^2)dt.$$

We wish to consider small fluctuations from the equilibrium point $X = x_0 = \frac{\lambda - \mu}{\kappa}$.
This state is quasi-stationary because there is always the possibility of extinction,
assuming that there will be stochastic fluctuations around that point (Pielou, 1969,
p. 27). Considering stochastic fluctuations we can write the equation

$$(45) \quad dX = (\lambda X - \mu X - \kappa X^2)dt + dz$$

where dz is the stochastic displacement from the deterministic rate of change.
We assume

$$Pr[dz = +1 | X] = \lambda X dt,$$
$$(46) \quad Pr[dz = -1 | X] = (\mu X + \kappa X^2)dt,$$
$$Pr[dz = 0 | X] = 1 - (\lambda X + \mu X + \kappa X^2)dt,$$
$$\text{as } dt \to 0.$$

At the equilibrium point

$$E(dz) = (+1)\lambda X dt + (-1)(\mu X + \kappa X^2)dt \Big|_{X=x_0}$$
$$(47) \qquad\qquad = 0,$$
$$Var(dz) = (+1)^2 \lambda X dt + (-1)^2 (\mu X + \kappa X^2)dt \Big|_{X=x_0}$$
$$\qquad\qquad = (\lambda x_0 + \mu x_0 + \kappa x_0^2)dt.$$

We want to find the mean and variance of X about the equilibrium value, $x_0 = \frac{(\lambda - \mu)}{\kappa}$, under the operation of dz, the stochastic fluctuation. Let X_t measure the deviation from the mean, i.e.

(48) $X_t = X - m$, where $m = E(X)$.

At time $t + dt$,

$$X_{t+dt} = X_t + (\lambda X - \mu X - \kappa X^2)dt + dz.$$

Taking expectations, we have from (47) that $E(dz) = 0$ and from (48) that

(49) $E(X_t) = 0$, $E(X_{t+dt}) = 0$,

so that

(50) $E[(\lambda X - \mu X - \kappa X^2)dt] = 0$.

But also

$$E[(\lambda X - \mu X - \kappa X^2)dt] = [(\lambda - \mu)m - \kappa E(X^2)]dt$$

(51) $= [(\lambda - \mu)m - \kappa m^2 - \kappa Var(X)]dt$

implies, taken with (50)

(52) $(\lambda - \mu)m = \kappa Var(X) + \kappa m^2$,

which can be written as

(53) $m = x_0 - \frac{Var(X)}{m}$.

Clearly then $m < x_0$, and assuming that $m \approx x_0$ we obtain the estimate

(54) $\hat{m} = x_0 - \frac{Var(X)}{x_0}$.

To find $Var(X)$, assume that X departs only slightly from x_0, and let $X = x_0(1 + u)$ with u small. We have

(55) $dX = x_0 du,$

and hence we write the stochastic equation (45) as

$$x_0 du = [\lambda x_0(1+u) - \mu x_0(1+u) - \kappa x_0^2(1+u)^2]dt + dz,$$

(56)
$$= \kappa x_0^2[-u(1+u)]dt + dz,$$

since $x_0 = (\lambda - \mu)/\kappa$. Dividing by x_0 gives

$$du = -\kappa x_0 u(1 + u)dt + \frac{1}{x_0} dz,$$

$$\approx -\kappa x_0 u dt + \frac{1}{x_0} dz,$$

since, for u small, $1 + u \approx 1$. From (57) we can obtain

(58) $(u + du)^2 = u^2(1 - \kappa x_0 dt)^2 + \frac{2u}{x_0}(1 - \kappa x_0 dt)dz + \frac{(dz)^2}{x_0^2}$.

We note that $E(dz) = 0$ implies

$$E[(dz)^2] = Var(dz)$$

and further that because we are in a state of stochastic equilibrium, $E(u) = 0$ and

$$E[(u + du)^2] = E[u^2] = Var(u).$$

Hence taking expectations of (58) yields

(59) $Var(u) = (1 - \kappa x_0 dt)^2 Var(u) + \frac{1}{x_0^2}[\lambda X + \mu X + \kappa X^2]dt.$

Neglecting terms in $(dt)^2$ gives

$$Var(u) = (1 - 2\kappa x_0 dt)Var(u) + \frac{1}{x_0^2}[\lambda X + \mu X + \kappa X^2]dt.$$

Letting $X \approx x_0$, we can write

$$Var(u) \approx (1 - 2\kappa x_0 dt)Var(u) + (\frac{\lambda + \mu}{x_0} + \kappa)dt$$

or equivalently upon simplifying

(60) $\text{Var(u)} \approx \dfrac{\lambda\kappa}{(\lambda-\mu)^2}$.

Now

(61) $\text{Var(X)} = x_o{}^2 \, \text{Var(u)}$

$\approx \lambda/\kappa.$

Substituting this result in (54) gives

$$\hat{m} \approx \frac{\lambda-\mu}{\kappa} - \frac{\lambda}{\lambda-\mu}$$

$$= x_0 - \frac{\lambda}{\lambda-\mu} \approx E(X).$$

Thus we have obtained approximate expressions for the mean and variance of X at stochastic equilibrium.

7. Van Kampen's Method

The following method is similar to the method of cumulants in that it is both continuous and yields a Gaussian process as an approximation. It is also interesting to note the mean and variance for the asymptotic distribution obtained by this method agree with those obtained by the method of stochastic linearization. Van Kampen (1973) presents this method as being generally applicable for finding asymptotic solutions of birth and death processes.

Suppose we expect X to be of order N, where

$$(62) \quad N = (\lambda - \mu)/\kappa$$

is the deterministic carrying capacity, and further that X has fluctuations of order $N^{\frac{1}{2}}$. We write

$$(63) \quad X = N\phi(t) + N^{\frac{1}{2}}y,$$

where ϕ is a function of time and y is new random variable. Equation (63) can be interpreted as a Taylor series expansion about X = N under the assumptions that

    i) for t large enough, $\phi(t) \approx 1$ does not depend upon t, at least

        approximately, and

    ii) The fluctuations in X, X - N, are such that $X - N = N^{\frac{1}{2}}y$.

We are, in effect, assuming that t is large enough so that X does not depend upon t, and in that sense the solution obtained will be asymptotic. Further, van Kampen assumes that N is large.

The density of the transformed variable y is written

$$(64) \quad q(y,t) = N^{\frac{1}{2}}p[N(t) + N^{\frac{1}{2}}y, t]$$

where p is the continuous form of the (really discrete) density of x, which satisfies the continuous analogue of the differential difference equation (20). By expanding into two Taylor series, (20) becomes

(65) $\quad \dfrac{\partial p}{\partial t} = \sum\limits_{n=1}^{\infty} \dfrac{(-1)^n}{n!} (\dfrac{\partial}{\partial x})^n \lambda x p(x,t) + \sum\limits_{n=1}^{\infty} \dfrac{(1)^n}{n!} (\dfrac{\partial}{\partial x})^n (\mu x + \kappa x^2) p(x,t)$

$$= \sum\limits_{n=1}^{\infty} \dfrac{1}{n!} (\dfrac{\partial}{\partial x})^n [\dfrac{\{(-1)^n \lambda + \mu\}}{(\lambda - \mu)} (\kappa N x) + \kappa x^2] p(x,t).$$

We write, after van Kampen,

(66) $\quad \dfrac{\partial p}{\partial t} = N^{\frac{1}{2}} \dfrac{\partial q}{\partial t} - \dfrac{\partial q}{\partial y} \dfrac{d\phi}{dt} .$

Thus, after transforming from x to y and making some algebraic manipulations, we have

(67) $\quad \dfrac{\partial q}{\partial t} - N^{\frac{1}{2}} \dfrac{\partial q}{\partial y} \dfrac{\partial \phi}{\partial t} = \sum\limits_{n=1}^{\infty} \dfrac{N^{(2 - \frac{n}{2})}}{n!} (\dfrac{\partial}{\partial y})^n [\dfrac{\{(-1)^n \lambda + \mu\}}{(\lambda - \mu)} \kappa(\phi + \dfrac{y}{N^{\frac{1}{2}}})$

$$+ \kappa(\phi^2 + \dfrac{2y\phi}{N^{\frac{1}{2}}} + \dfrac{y^2}{N})] q(y,t)$$

Equate terms with positive powers of N on both sides of equation (67), so that

$$\kappa N^{\frac{3}{2}}(\phi^2 - \phi) \dfrac{\partial q}{\partial y} = -N^{\frac{1}{2}} \dfrac{\partial q}{\partial y} \dfrac{d\phi}{dt} ,$$

which implies

$$\dfrac{d\phi}{dt} = -\kappa N(\phi^2 - \phi).$$

Letting $T = \kappa N t$ yields

(68) $\quad \dfrac{d\phi}{dT} = \phi(1 - \phi),$

which integrates to

(69) $\quad \phi(T) = \dfrac{e^T}{1 + e^T} .$

We transform equation (67) to the T-scale giving

$$\frac{\partial q}{\partial T} - N^{\frac{1}{2}} \frac{\partial q}{\partial y} \frac{d\phi}{dT} = \sum_{n=1}^{\infty} N^{(1 - \frac{n}{2})} \frac{1}{n!} (\frac{\partial}{\partial y})^n [\frac{\{(-1)^n \lambda + \mu\}}{(\lambda - \mu)} (\phi + \frac{y}{N^{\frac{1}{2}}})$$

(70)

$$+ (\phi^2 + \frac{2y\phi}{N^{\frac{1}{2}}} + \frac{y^2}{N})] q(y,t).$$

We now equate, in (70), terms in N^0:

$$\frac{\partial q}{\partial T} = \frac{1}{2} (\frac{\partial}{\partial y})^2 [\frac{(\lambda+\mu)}{(\lambda-\mu)} \phi + \phi^2] q(y,t) + \frac{\partial}{\partial y} (-y + 2y\phi) q(y,t)$$

(71)

$$= (2\phi - 1) \frac{\partial}{\partial y} (yq) + \frac{1}{2} \phi [\frac{(\lambda+\mu)}{(\lambda-\mu)} + \phi] \frac{\partial^2 q}{\partial y^2} .$$

As per van Kampen (1961), we can transform this into an equation for which the solution is known. Let

(72) $s(T) = -\log \phi(1 - \phi) - \log 4,$

and note that $ds/dT = 2\phi - 1$. Under this transformation, (71) becomes

(73) $$\frac{\partial q}{\partial s} = \frac{\partial}{\partial y} (qy) + \frac{\phi[\frac{(\lambda+\mu)}{(\lambda-\mu)} + \phi]}{2(2\phi - 1)} \frac{\partial^2 q}{\partial y^2} .$$

Applying the additional transformations

$$y = ze^{-s}, q = e^s Q(z,s),$$

we obtain

(74) $$\frac{\partial Q}{\partial s} = \frac{\phi[\frac{(\lambda+\mu)}{(\lambda-\mu)} + \phi]}{2(2\phi - 1)} e^{2s} \frac{\partial^2 Q}{\partial z^2} .$$

The solution to this equation is given by Chandrasekhar (1943):

(75) $$Q(z,s) = \frac{1}{(4\pi I)^{\frac{1}{2}}} \exp [-\frac{(z - z_0)^2}{4I}],$$

where $I = \int_0^s \frac{\phi[\frac{(\lambda+\mu)}{(\lambda-\mu)} + \phi]}{2(2\phi - 1)} e^{2s} ds.$

We note that in the transformation (72), $s(0) = 0$ is required because Chandrasekhar's solution assumes a starting point at $s = 0$. Since our process starts at $t = 0$, we want $s(0) = 0$ so that the original and transformed starting points correspond. The term z_0 is obtained from initial conditions. We have $x = 1$ at $t = 0$ with probability one, so that

$$(76) \quad y_0 = N^{-\frac{1}{2}} - \frac{N^{\frac{1}{2}}}{2},$$

and

$$(77) \quad z_0 = e^{s(0)} y_0 = N^{-\frac{1}{2}} - \frac{N^{\frac{1}{2}}}{2}.$$

See Appendix I for an evaluation of $I = I(t)$. We transform equation (75) back to x and t, obtaining

$$(78) \quad p(x,t) = \frac{[e^{(\lambda-\mu)t} + 2 + e^{-(\lambda-\mu)t}]}{[64\ NI(t)]^{\frac{1}{2}}} \exp\{\frac{-[x(e^{(\lambda-\mu)t} + 2 + e^{-(\lambda-\mu)t}) - Ne^{(\lambda-\mu)t} + N - 4]^2}{64NI(t)}\}$$

With suitable rearrangements we can write

$$(79) \quad p(x,t) = \frac{1}{\sqrt{2\pi c_2(t)}} \exp\{-\frac{[x - c_1(t)]^2}{2c_2(t)}\},$$

where

$$c_1(t) = \frac{Ne^{(\lambda-\mu)t} - N + 4}{J(t)},$$

$$c_2(t) = \frac{32NI(t)}{[J(t)]^2},$$

and

$$I(t) = \frac{1}{32(\lambda-\mu)}[2(2\lambda+\mu)(\lambda-\mu)t - 5\lambda - (\lambda+\mu)e^{-(\lambda-\mu)t} + (5\lambda+\mu)e^{(\lambda-\mu)t} + e^{2(\lambda-\mu)t}],$$

$$J(t) = e^{(\lambda-\mu)t} + 2 + e^{-(\lambda-\mu)t}.$$

From (79) we immediately see that this approximation is normal with stochastic mean $c_1(t)$ and stochastic variance $c_2(t)$. According to van Kampen, it would be possible to obtain higher order approximations by this method by considering terms in powers of $N^{-\frac{1}{2}}$ in equation (70), although this was not attempted here.

Examining

$$\lim_{t \to \infty} c_1(t) = N = \frac{(\lambda - \mu)}{\kappa} \, ,$$

(80)

$$\lim_{t \to \infty} c_2(t) = \frac{\lambda}{\kappa} \, ,$$

we see that the asymptotic variance from van Kampen's method agrees with the result obtained by stochastic linearization. Also, the stochastic mean has the same asymptotic value as the deterministic solution. These results are an improvement over those obtained by the cumulant method. But if we examine the stationary distribution, we find

$$\lim_{t \to \infty} M(\theta, t) = \lim_{t \to \infty} \exp[c_1(t)\theta + c_2(t)\frac{\theta^2}{2}],$$

$$= \exp[\lim_{t \to \infty} c_1(t)\theta + \lim_{t \to \infty} c_2(t) \frac{\theta^2}{2}] \, ,$$

$$= \exp[(\frac{\lambda - \mu}{\kappa})\theta + (\frac{\lambda}{2\kappa})\theta^2].$$

Hence the stationary distribution for the approximation is Normal $[\frac{(\lambda-\mu)}{\kappa} , \frac{\lambda}{\kappa}]$, which does not agree with the degenerate distribution, i.e., unit mass at $X = 0$, obtained for the exact process. It must also be noted as a disadvantage that the approximation is continuous but the exact process is discrete. The assumptions i) and ii) really tell us that we are finding an asymptotic solution, given that X is expected to be of order N. The values of t for which the approximation is valid are such that $\phi(t)$ is approximately one. This in turn depends upon the parameters λ and μ. See Figures 6, 7, and 8 for plots of the stochastic mean and variance obtained by van Kampen's approach, together with $\phi(t)$ so as to indicate the region of validity. We see that, by the time $\phi(t)$ is close to one, both mean and variance have stabilized to their asymptotic values. Thus applying the region of validity we obtain no more information from van Kampen's method than from the considerably more straightforward stochastic linearization argument.

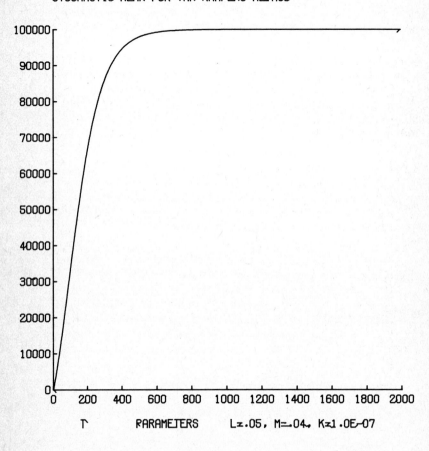

STOCHASTIC MEAN FOR VAN KAMPENS METHOD

T   PARAMETERS   L=.05, M=.04, K=1.0E-07

T VERSUS X2   200 VALUES

FIGURE **6a**

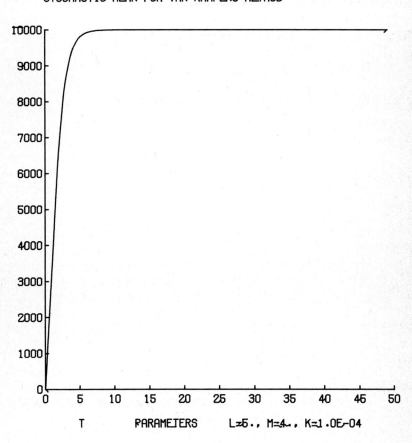

STOCHASTIC MEAN FOR VAN KAMPENS METHOD

T   PARAMETERS   L=5., M=4., K=1.0E-04

. T VERSUS X2   50 VALUES

FIGURE **6b**

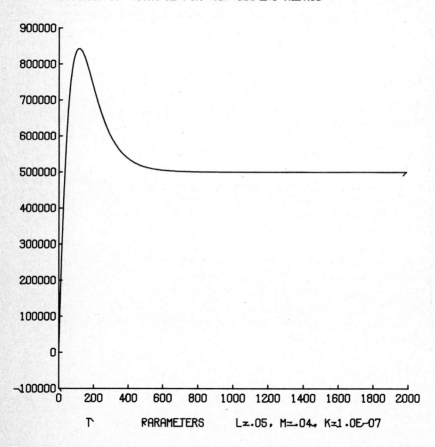

STOCHASTIC VARIANCE FOR VAN KAMPENS METHOD

T   PARAMETERS   L=.05, M=.04, K=1.0E-07

T VERSUS Y3   200 VALUES

FIGURE **7a**

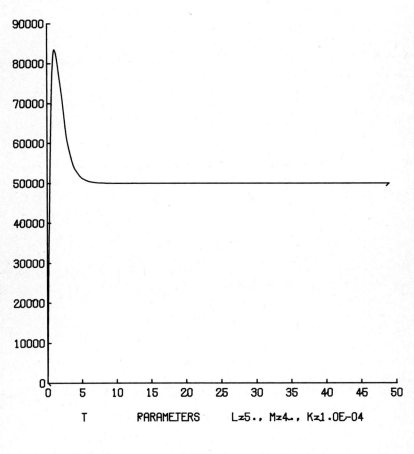

STOCHASTIC VARIANCE FOR VAN KAMPENS METHOD

T   PARAMETERS   L=5., M=4., K=1.0E-04

T VERSUS Y3   50 VALUES

FIGURE **7b**

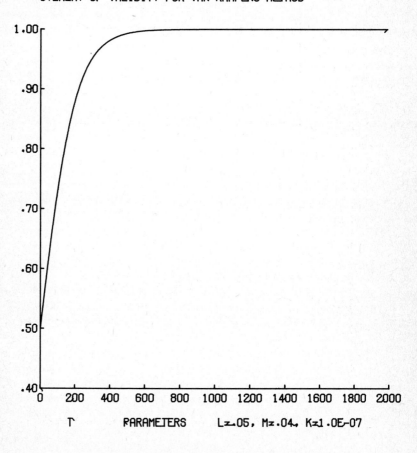

OVERLAY OF VALIDITY FOR VAN KAMPENS METHOD

T   PARAMETERS   L=.05, M=.04, K=1.0E-07

T VERSUS RHI   200 VALUES

FIGURE **8a**

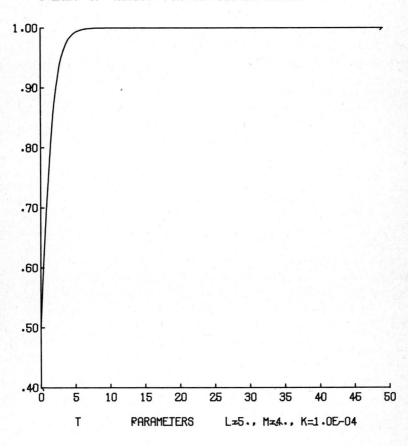

OVERLAY OF VALIDITY FOR VAN KAMPENS METHOD

T   PARAMETERS   L≠5., M≠4., K=1.0E-04

T VERSUS RHI   50 VALUES

FIGURE **8b**

8.   Method of Linearized Transition Probabilities

Suppose we examine the transition probability for deaths,

(81) $Pr[\Delta X(t) = -1 | X(t) = n] = f_{-1}(n)\Delta t + 0(\Delta t)$

where

(82) $f_{-1}(n) = \mu n + \kappa n^2.$

It is the nonlinearity of f_{-1} that creates the difficulty in solving the differential equations for our stochastic process. The method of linearized transition probabilities approximates f_{-1} by writing

(83) $f_{-1}(n) \approx \mu n + \kappa \hat{X}(t)n$

where $\hat{X}(t)$ is a nonrandom function of time that approximates $X = n$, the number of tumor cells. Thus our transition probabilities become linear with respect to $X = n$ but non-homogeneous with respect to time, t. This is a non-homogeneous birth and death process for which the general solution can be found in Bailey (1964). All that remains is the choice of $\hat{X}$. The first choice that came to mind was the stochastic mean; but as this is unavailable, the deterministic equation (14) is used. Experience with nonlinear birth and death processes has indicated that the stochastic mean is at least close to the deterministic solution. See Feller (1939) for the logistic process and Bailey (1964) for epidemics. In the case of the simple linear birth and death process, the stochastic mean and deterministic equation are identical.

Bailey gives as the solution for the time non-homogeneous birth and death process

(84) $P(z,t) = 1 + [\dfrac{e^{\rho(t)}}{z-1} - \int_0^t \lambda(T)e^{\rho(T)} dT]^{-1}$

$\qquad$ where $\rho(t) = \int_0^t [\mu(T) - \lambda(T)]dT,$

and $P(z,t) = \sum_{i=0}^{\infty} p_i(t)z^i$ is the probability generating function. In our case

(85) $\quad \lambda(t) = \lambda, \quad \mu(t) = \mu + \kappa\hat{X}(t),$

and using

(86) $\quad \hat{X}(t) = \dfrac{(\lambda-\mu)}{(\lambda-\mu-\kappa)e^{-(\lambda-\mu)t} + \kappa},$

we can evaluate

$$\rho(t) = \int_0^t [\mu-\lambda + \frac{\kappa(\lambda-\mu)}{\{(\lambda-\mu-\kappa)e^{-(\lambda-\mu)T} + \kappa\}}]dT$$

(87)

$$= \log[\frac{(\lambda-\mu-\kappa)e^{-(\lambda-\mu)t} + \kappa}{(\lambda-\mu)}],$$

and so

(88) $\quad e^{\rho(t)} = \dfrac{(\lambda-\mu-\kappa)e^{-(\lambda-\mu)t} + \kappa}{(\lambda-\mu)}$

We also have

(89) $\quad \int_0^t \lambda(T)e^{\rho(T)}dT = \int_0^t \dfrac{\lambda[(\lambda-\mu-\kappa)e^{-(\lambda-\mu)T} + \kappa]}{(\lambda-\mu)} \, dT,$

$$= \frac{1}{(\lambda-\mu)} [\lambda\kappa t + \frac{\lambda(\lambda-\mu-\kappa)}{(\lambda-\mu)} \{1 - e^{-(\lambda-\mu)t}\}],$$

so that

(90) $\quad P(z,t) = 1+(\lambda-\mu)[\dfrac{\{(\lambda-\mu-\kappa)e^{-(\lambda-\mu)t} + \kappa\}}{z - 1} - \lambda\kappa t - \dfrac{\lambda(\lambda-\mu-\kappa)}{(\lambda-\mu)}\{1-e^{-(\lambda-\mu)t}\}]^{-1}.$

The stochastic mean can be expressed as

(91) $\quad c_1(t) = \dfrac{\partial P}{\partial z}\Big|_{z=1}.$

Since

(92) $\quad \dfrac{\partial P}{\partial z} = \dfrac{(\lambda-\mu)[(\lambda-\mu-\kappa)e^{-(\lambda-\mu)t} + \kappa]}{[(\lambda-\mu-\kappa)e^{-(\lambda-\mu)t} +\kappa-(z-1)\lambda(\lambda-\mu-\kappa)\{\frac{\kappa t}{(\lambda-\mu-\kappa)} + \frac{\{1-e^{-(\lambda-\mu)t}\}}{(\lambda-\mu)}\}]^2}$

we obtain

(93) $\quad c_1(t) = \dfrac{(\lambda-\mu)}{(\lambda-\mu-\kappa)e^{-(\lambda-\mu)t} + \kappa}$.

Hence the stochastic mean for the method of linearized transition probabilities is equivalent to the deterministic equation. We find the stochastic variance from

(94) $\quad c_2(t) = [\dfrac{\partial^2 P}{\partial z^2} + \dfrac{\partial P}{\partial z} - (\dfrac{\partial P}{\partial z})^2]\Big|_{z=1}$

Now

(95) $\quad \dfrac{\partial^2 P}{\partial z^2} = \dfrac{2(\lambda-\mu)[\lambda\kappa t + \frac{\lambda(\lambda-\mu-\kappa)}{(\lambda-\mu)}\{1 - e^{-(\lambda-\mu)t}\}][(\lambda-\mu-\kappa)e^{-(\lambda-\mu)t} + \kappa]}{[(\lambda-\mu-\kappa)e^{-(\lambda-\mu)t} + \kappa-(z-1)\lambda(\lambda-\mu-\kappa)\left[\frac{\kappa t}{(\lambda-\mu-\kappa)} + \frac{\{1-e^{-(\lambda-\mu)t}\}}{(\lambda-\mu)}\right]]^3}$

This together with (92) yields

(96) $\quad c_2(t) = \dfrac{2\lambda\kappa[(\lambda-\mu)t+1] + (\lambda-\mu)(\lambda+\mu+\kappa) - (\lambda+\mu)(\lambda-\mu-\kappa)e^{-(\lambda-\mu)t}}{[(\lambda-\mu-\kappa)e^{-(\lambda-\mu)t} + \kappa]^2}$

See Figures 3 (pages 24, 25, 26, 27, 28, and 29) and 9 for plots of the stochastic mean and variance. In Appendix IV we derive the probability density,

(97) $\quad p_n(t) = \dfrac{(\lambda-\mu)}{h(t)} [\dfrac{h_2(t)}{h(t)}]^{n-1} [1 - \dfrac{h_2(t)}{h(t)}]$, for $n \geq 1$,

where $\quad h_1(t) = (\lambda-\mu-\kappa)e^{-(\lambda-\mu)t} + \kappa$,

$\qquad\qquad h_2(t) = \dfrac{\lambda(\lambda-\mu-\kappa)}{(\lambda-\mu)} [1 - e^{-(\lambda-\mu)t}] + \lambda\kappa t$,

$\qquad\qquad h(t) = h_1(t) + h_2(t)$,

and

(98) $\quad p_0(t) = 1 - \dfrac{(\lambda-\mu)}{h(t)}$.

This latter quantity is the probability of extinction of a tumor colony.

Substituting for $h(t)$ in (96) yields

(99) $\quad p_0(t) = 1 - \dfrac{(\lambda-\mu)^2}{\kappa(\lambda-\mu)(\lambda t+1) + (\lambda-\mu-\kappa)[\lambda-\mu e^{-(\lambda-\mu)t}]}$.

From equations (90), (93), (96) and (99), it is easy to obtain the asymptotic properties

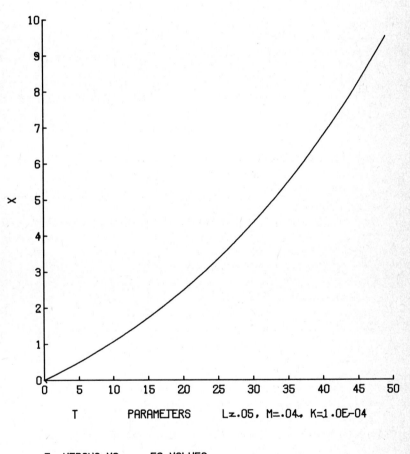

STOCHASTIC VARIANCE FOR LINEARIZED TRANSITION RROBABILITIES

T   PARAMETERS   L=.05, M=.04, K=1.0E-04

T   VERSUS X2   50 VALUES

FIGURE **9a**

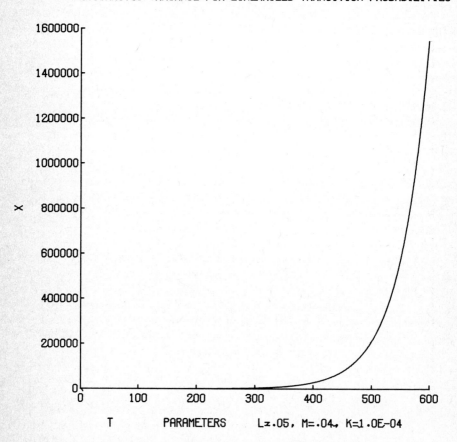

STOCHASTIC VARIANCE FOR LINEARIZED TRANSITION PROBABILITIES

T   PARAMETERS   L=.05, M=.04, K=1.0E-04

T VERSUS X2   600 VALUES

FIGURE **9b**

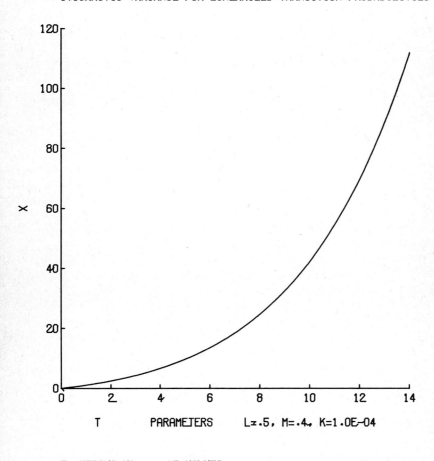

STOCHASTIC VARIANCE FOR LINEARIZED TRANSITION PROBABILITIES

T   PARAMETERS   L=.5, M=.4, K=1.0E-04

T   VERSUS X2.   15 VALUES

FIGURE **9c**

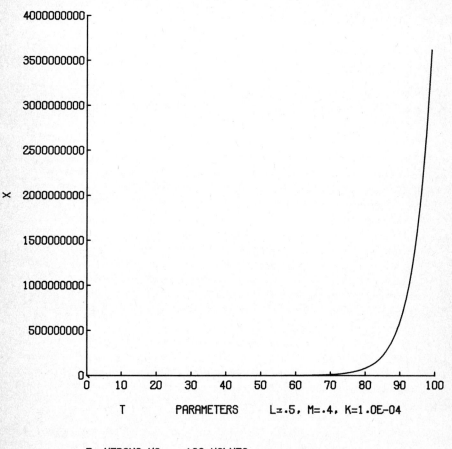

STOCHASTIC VARIANCE FOR LINEARIZED TRANSITION PROBABILITIES

T   PARAMETERS   L=.5, M=.4, K=1.0E-04

T   VERSUS X2   100 VALUES

FIGURE **9d**

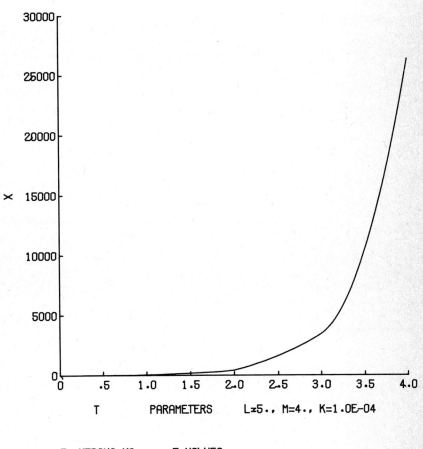

STOCHASTIC VARIANCE FOR LINEARIZED TRANSITION PROBABILITIES

T   PARAMETERS   L=5., M=4., K=1.0E-04

T   VERSUS X2   5 VALUES

FIGURE **9e**

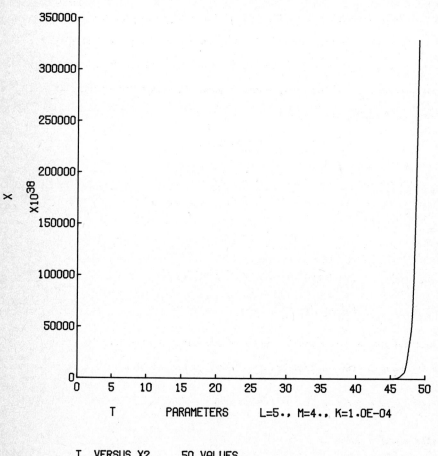

FIGURE **9f**

$$\lim_{t \to \infty} P(z,t) = 1,$$

$$\lim_{t \to \infty} c_1(t) = (\lambda-\mu)/\kappa,$$

(100)

$$\lim_{t \to \infty} c_2(t) = +\infty,$$

$$\lim_{t \to \infty} p_0(t) = 1.$$

Thus, this approximation satisfies the stationary distribution of the exact process, as well as the asymptotic probability of extinction. The approximate stochastic mean is equal to the deterministic solution, which we expect to exhibit similar properties to the exact mean. In the subsequent analysis we develop a measure of how closely they agree. Note that the variance (96) does not converge in Cesaro mean since its leading term

$$te^{2(\lambda-\mu)t}$$

does not so converge. To see this, we evaluate

$$\lim_{c \to \infty} \frac{1}{c} \sum_{t=0}^{c-1} te^{2(\lambda-\mu)t}$$

$$\geq \lim_{c \to \infty} \frac{1}{c} \sum_{t=0}^{c-1} t$$

$$= \lim_{c \to \infty} \frac{c-1}{2} = +\infty$$

It is appropriate to consider whether the exact process converges in quadratic mean to the mean of the approximation. Recall that equation (19) tell us that

$$\lim_{t \to \infty} p_n(t) = 0 \text{ for } n \neq 0$$

(101)

$$\lim_{t \to \infty} p_0(t) = 1,$$

for the exact process. Thus

$$(102) \quad E[X - \hat{X}]^2 = \sum_{n=0}^{\infty} [n - \hat{X}]^2 p_n(t)$$

will have the limiting value

(103) $\quad \lim_{t \to \infty} E[X - \hat{X}] = \lim_{t \to \infty} \hat{X}^2 = \dfrac{(\lambda-\mu)^2}{\kappa^2}$,

and we do not have the desired convergence in quadratic mean. But since equations (101 – 103) apply to the approximate process as well, neither does the approximation converge in quadratic mean to $\hat{X}$. However, it is easy to see that both the exact process and the approximation converge in quadratic mean to zero. There is an apparent contradiction that as $t \to \infty$, the approximate stochastic mean approaches an asymptotic upper limit, and the approximate stochastic variance increases without bound, whereas the stationary distribution has unit mass at $X = 0$. A simple example of this kind of phenomenon is as follows: as t gets large, there is a small probability of having a tumor grow without bound and one minus that small probability of being extinct ($X = 0$). For instance take

$\quad \Pr[X(t) = (\dfrac{\lambda-\mu}{\kappa})t] = \dfrac{1}{t}$,

(104) $\quad \Pr[X(t) = 0] = 1 - \dfrac{1}{t}$, $\qquad\qquad$ (for $t \neq 0$)

$\quad \Pr[X(t) = \text{all other values}] = 0$,

so that

$\quad E[X(t)] = \dfrac{\lambda-\mu}{\kappa}$ for all $t \neq 0$

but $\lim_{t \to \infty} \Pr[X(t) = 0] = 1$.

We introduce (104) not to imply that this is true for the approximation obtained by the method of linearized transition probabilities, but as an example of how a stationary distribution degenerate at $X = 0$ can be obtained for a process with nonzero stochastic mean for all nonzero t. This kind of phenomenon characterizes the exact model as well. At $t = +\infty$, which is never realized in practice, the tumor would be extinct with probability one. We see then that the approximation exhibits the erratic growth pattern that is consistent with what we would expect from a colony of tumor cells.

The method of linearized transition probabilities has further advantages. It is the only one of the methods that preserves the discreteness of the original process, as well as its Markov properties. Not to be ignored is its relative ease of application. Provided that the approximating function, $\hat{X}(t)$, is such that the integrals in (84) can be evaluated, the solution for the probability generating function follows almost immediately. Furthermore we can generalize the results obtained above in the following theorem.

Theorem

Let a Markov process $X_1(t)$ be defined by the transition probabilities

$$\Pr[\Delta X_1(t) = +1 \,|\, X_1(t) = n] = f_{+1}(n)\Delta t + 0(\Delta t),$$

(105) $$\Pr[\Delta X_1(t) = -1 \,|\, X_1(t) = n] = f_{-1}(n)\Delta t + 0(\Delta t),$$

$$\Pr[\Delta X_1(t) = 0 \,|\, X_1(t) = n] = 1 - [f_{+1}(n) + f_{-1}(n)]\Delta t + 0(\Delta t),$$

where $$f_{+1}(n) = \sum_{i=0}^{\infty} a_i n^i,$$

$$f_{-1}(n) = \sum_{i=0}^{\infty} b_i n^i,$$

$X_1(0) = a$ with probability one, and a, a_i, b_i are constants for all i. We define the deterministic formulation, $\hat{X}(t)$, by the differential equation

(106) $$\frac{d\hat{X}(t)}{dt} = f_{+1}[\hat{X}(t)] - f_{-1}[\hat{X}(t)]$$

$$= \sum_{i=0}^{\infty} a_i [\hat{X}(t)]^i - \sum_{i=0}^{\infty} b_i [\hat{X}(t)]^i$$

We now define an "approximation" Markov process, $X_2(t)$, by the transition probabilities

$$\Pr[\Delta X_2(t) = +1 \,|\, X_2(t) = n] = g_{+1}(n,t)\Delta t + 0(\Delta t),$$

(107) $$\Pr[\Delta X_2(t) = -1 \,|\, X_2(t) = n] = g_{-1}(n,t)\Delta t + 0(\Delta t),$$

$$\Pr[\Delta X_2(t) = 0 \,|\, X_2(t) = n] = 1 - [g_{+1}(n,t) + g_{-1}(n,t)]\Delta t + 0(\Delta t),$$

where $g_{+1}(n,t) = a_0 + [\sum_{i=1}^{\infty} a_i \{\hat{X}(t)\}^{i-1}]n = a_0 + \lambda(t)n,$

$$g_{-1}(n,t) = b_0 + [\sum_{i=1}^{\infty} b_i \{\hat{X}(t)\}^{i-1}]n = b_0 + \mu(t)n,$$

$X_2(0) = a$ with probability one where a is a constant and a_i, b_i are define above. Then, the stochastic mean of $X_2(t)$, $c_1^{X_2}(t)$, will be equal to the solution of the deterministic equation defined by (106).

Proof

The stochastic process $X_2(t)$ is a birth and death process that has transition probabilities that are linear in n but nonhomogeneous in t. Parzen (1962, pp. 300-301) gives the partial differential equation for the probability generating function, $P_{X_2}(z,t) = \sum_{n=0}^{\infty} p_n^{X_2}(t)z^n$, as (changing to our notation so that the sub or superscript X_i refers to the stochastic process X_i)

$$(108) \quad \frac{\partial P_{X_2}(z,t)}{\partial t} = \frac{\partial P_{X_2}(z,t)}{\partial z}(z-1)[z\lambda(t) - \mu(t)] + (a_0 - b_0)(z - 1)P_{X_2}(z,t).$$

Note that we have summed over all states n and consider s = 0 in Parzen's notation, dropping one of his subscripts. Applying the transformation for the cumulant generating function,

$$(109) \quad C_{X_2}(\theta,t) = \sum_{i=1}^{\infty} c_i^{X_2}(t)\frac{\theta^i}{i!},$$

$$= \log P_{X_2}(e^{\theta},t),$$

we obtain the equation

$$(110) \quad \frac{\partial C_{X_2}(\theta,t)}{\partial t} = \frac{\partial C_{X_2}(\theta,t)}{\partial \theta}(1 - e^{-\theta})[e^{\theta}\lambda(t) - \mu(t)] + (a_0 - b_0)(e^{\theta} - 1).$$

Now

$$\frac{\partial C_{X_2}(\theta,t)}{\partial t} = \sum_{i=1}^{\infty} \frac{\partial c_i^{X_2}(t)}{\partial t} \cdot \frac{\theta^i}{i!} ,$$

(111)

$$\frac{\partial C_{X_2}(\theta,t)}{\partial \theta} = \sum_{i=1}^{\infty} c_i^{X_2}(t) \frac{\theta^{i-1}}{(i-1)!} ,$$

so that equating coefficients of θ on both sides of (110), using the series representation of e^θ as well as (111), yields

(112) $$\frac{dc_1^{X_2}(t)}{dt} = c_1^{X_2}(t)[\lambda(t) - \mu(t)] + (a_0 - b_0),$$

$$= c_1^{X_2}(t)[\sum_{i=1}^{\infty} a_i\{\hat{X}(t)\}^{i-1} - \sum_{i=1}^{\infty} b_i\{\hat{X}(t)\}^{i-1}] + (a_0 - b_0).$$

We see at once from the definition (106) of $\hat{X}(t)$ that

(113) $$c_1^{X_2}(t) = \hat{X}(t)$$

is the unique non-trivial solution of (112). Since the first cumulant is the stochastic mean, this completes the proof.

Due to the polynomial form of f_{+1} and f_{-1}, the above theorem will apply to epidemic models and competition and predation processes. Further the case of immigration or mutation can be automatically incorporated by inclusion of the n^0 term in the transition probabilities.

The method of linearized transition probabilities allows some insight into the nature of the error caused by the linearization. In the notation of the theorem, consider

$$f_{-1} = \mu n + \kappa n^2,$$

(114)

$$g_{-1} = \mu n + \kappa n\hat{X},$$

Where $$\hat{X} = -\frac{(\lambda-\mu)}{(\lambda-\mu-\kappa)e^{-(\lambda-\mu)t} + \kappa} .$$

Of course for births, $f_{+1} = g_{+1} = n$, there is no error incurred. For

$$X_1 = n < \hat{X} : f_{-1} < g_{-1},$$

(115) $\quad X_1 = n = \hat{X} : f_{-1} = g_{-1},$

$$X_1 = n > \hat{X} : f_{-1} > g_{-1},$$

so that when realizations of the exact process, $X_1(t)$, are less than $\hat{X}$, the approximation process, $X_2(t)$, "dies too soon". This will be aggravated for small X_1 and large t, when $\hat{X}$ is close to $(\lambda-\mu)/\kappa$, its asymptotic upper limit. On the other hand, for X_1 greater than $\hat{X}$, the approximation X_2 "doesn't die fast enough". This will be a problem for large X_1 and small t (not a very likely event), or very large X_1 ($\gg (\lambda-\mu)/\kappa$) and any t. We derive an analytic measure for this discrepancy,

$$\Delta = f_{-1} - g_{-1}$$

(116) $\quad = \kappa n^2 - \kappa n \hat{X}$

$$= \kappa n (n - \hat{X}).$$

Taking expectations with respect to X_1, we have

(117) $\quad E(\Delta) = \kappa E(X_1{}^2) - \kappa \hat{X} E(X_1),$

$$= \kappa c_2^{X_1}(t) + \kappa c_1^{X_1}(t) [c_1^{X_1}(t) - \hat{X}(t)].$$

Unfortunately, $c_2^{X_1}$ and $c_1^{X_1}$ are unavailable, so that we cannot compute $E(\Delta)$ exactly. But taking expectations in (116) with respect to the approximate process X_2, we obtain

$$\hat{E}(\Delta) = \kappa c_2^{X_2}(t),$$

(118) $\quad = \dfrac{2\lambda\kappa^2[(\lambda-\mu)t+1] + \kappa(\lambda-\mu)(\lambda+\mu+\kappa) - \kappa(\lambda+\mu)(\lambda-\mu-\kappa)e^{-(\lambda-\mu)t}}{[(\lambda-\mu-\kappa)e^{-(\lambda-\mu)t}]^2},$

$$\lim_{t\to\infty} \hat{E}(\Delta) = +\infty.$$

See Figure 9 (pages 63-68) for plots of $c_2^{X_2}$. Note that $\hat{E}(\Delta)$ decreases with decreasing κ, assuming that $(\lambda-\mu) \gg \kappa$. But the leading term in (118) increases proportionally to

$$te^{2(\lambda-\mu)t}$$

so that $\hat{E}(\Delta)$ rapidly becomes very large.

Equation (118) is related to a result of Feller (1939). He examines the differential equation for the stochastic mean [see (33)],

$$(119) \quad \frac{dc_1^{X_1}}{dt} = (\lambda-\mu)c_1^{X_1} - \kappa(c_1^{X_1})^2 - \kappa c_2^{X_1}.$$

The first two terms will be explained by the deterministic equation defined by (13), and the last term by random fluctuations. Thus Feller finds the difference between the deterministic equation and the true stochastic mean is proportional to the variance of the exact process. Since the variance is non-negative, the deterministic equation will be greater than or equal to the exact stochastic mean. Thus it is an overestimate. Notice also that our result (118) is analogous to Feller's.

The above differential equations approach suggests a measure of the error in the approximate variance as well. Consider the equation for $c_2^{X_1}$ from (33),

$$(120) \quad \frac{dc_2^{X_1}}{dt} = (\lambda+\mu)c_1^{X_1} + 2(\lambda-\mu)c_2^{X_1} + \kappa c_2^{X_1} + \kappa(c_1^{X_1})^2 - 2\kappa(c_3^{X_1} + 2c_1^{X_1}c_2^{X_1}).$$

The corresponding equation for $c_2^{X_2}$ can be found by examining coefficients of θ^2 in (110) for the case $\lambda(t) = \lambda$, $\mu(t) = \mu + \kappa\hat{X}(t)$. It is

$$(121) \quad \frac{dc_2^{X_2}}{dt} = (\lambda+\mu)c_1^{X_2} + 2(\lambda-\mu)c_2^{X_2} + \kappa(c_1^{X_2})^2 - 2\kappa c_1^{X_2}c_2^{X_2}.$$

Equations (120) and (121) would be equivalent if (121) contained the additional terms

$$(122) \quad \kappa c_2^{X_2} - 2\kappa c_1^{X_2}c_2^{X_2} - 2\kappa c_3^{X_2}.$$

It would then seem that the effect of the approximation on the variance is of more complicated nature than on the mean. However, in either case, the discrepancy is proportional to κ. This is reasonable since as $\kappa \to 0$ the exact process approaches the linearity that is achieved at $\kappa = 0$, at which point the approximation is equivalent to the exact process.

We can give an heuristic interpretation of the error in the variance (96). Suppose we assume that the mean of X_1 is approximately $\hat{X}$ and examine the comparative dispersion of X_1 and X_2 around $\hat{X}$, remembering that the variance is a measure of that dispersion. Equations (105) tell us that X_2 tends to be more greatly dispersed about $\hat{X}$ since its death transition probabilities are less than those of X_1 for values greater than $\hat{X}$ and its death transition probabilities are greater than those of X_1 for values less than $\hat{X}$, birth transition probabilities being equal. Thus we can, although admittedly non-rigorously, consider the variance of X_2 as an upper bound for the variance of X_1. The crucial assumption is that $\hat{X}$ is very nearly the mean of the exact process; for if $\hat{X}$ differs greatly from the true mean, the argument does not apply. Under the assumption that the mean and variance of the approximation are overestimates, it follows from (107) and (108) that

$$(123) \quad \hat{E}(\Delta) \geq E(\Delta).$$

In other words, $c_2^{X_2} \geq c_2^{X_1}$ and $c_1^{X_2} \geq c_1^{X_1}$ imply that

$$\kappa c_2^{X_1} + \kappa c_1^{X_1}[c_1^{X_1} - c_1^{X_2}] \leq \kappa c_2^{X_2}.$$

Thus we expect $\hat{E}(\Delta)$ to be an overestimate of the expected error in transition probabilities.

Since so little of an exact nature is known for the nonlinear birth and death process (2), a small computer simulation was made to compare with the results of the linearized transition probabilities approximation (93), (96), and (99). The Fortran program used is given in Appendix III, developed by Chapman (1971). Figures 10a-10e are comparisons of the simulation mean to the deterministic mean for $\mu = .3$, $\kappa = 1.6 \times 10^{-2}$ and values λ ranging from .5 to 2.0. In all cases the simulation was iterated twenty times. The plots show the approximate mean is an overestimate, as we expect from theoretical considerations. Note that van Kampen's mean is even more of an overestimate, since it converges to the asymptotic value even faster than the solution for the deterministic equation (see Figure 6, pages

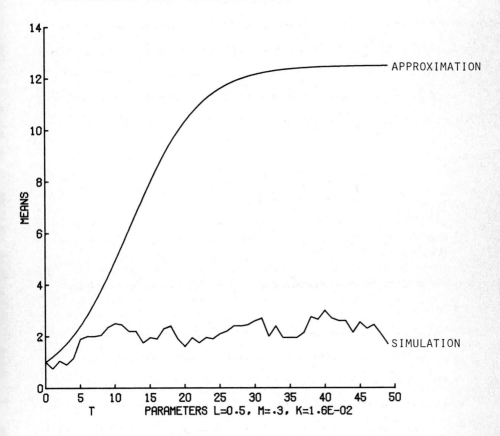

SIMULATION MEAN VERSUS APPROXIMATE MEAN

T   VERSUS AMEAN   50 VALUES
T   VERSUS XMEAN   50 VALUES

FIGURE **10a**

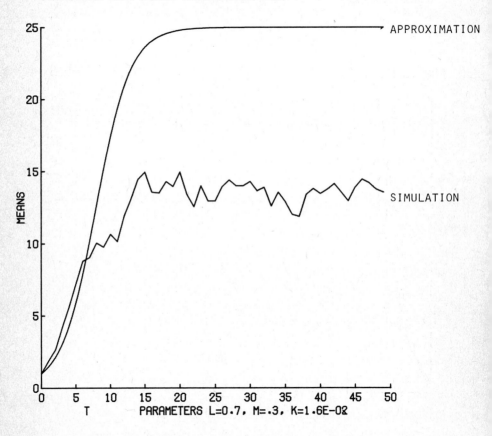

SIMULATION MEAN VERSUS APPROXIMATE MEAN

T   VERSUS AMEAN   50 VALUES
T   VERSUS XMEAN   50 VALUES

FIGURE **10b**

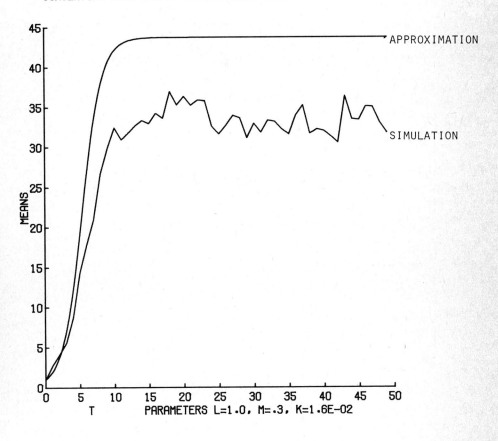

SIMULATION MEAN VERSUS APPROXIMATE MEAN

T   VERSUS AMEAN   50 VALUES
T   VERSUS XMEAN   50 VALUES

FIGURE 10c

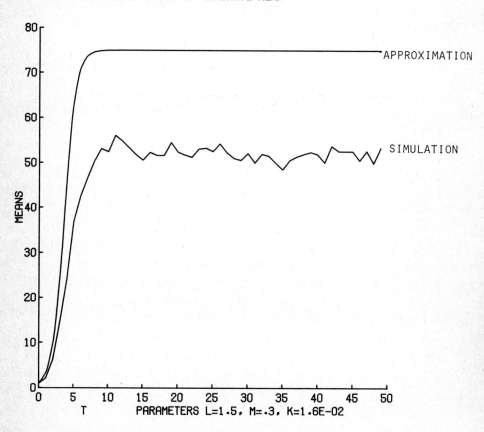

SIMULATION MEAN VERSUS APPROXIMATE MEAN

T   VERSUS AMEAN   50 VALUES
T   VERSUS XMEAN   50 VALUES

FIGURE **10d**

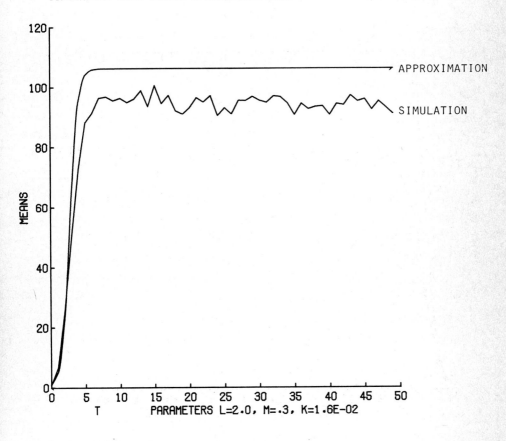

SIMULATION MEAN VERSUS APPROXIMATE MEAN

| T | VERSUS AMEAN | 50 VALUES |
| T | VERSUS XMEAN | 50 VALUES |

FIGURE **10e**

54-55). Clearly the results improve as λ increases. Why this should be follows from a consideration of the conditional probability of a birth or death, given that an event has occurred, i.e.

$$\Pr[\text{Birth at } t \mid \text{Event has occurred at } t] = \frac{\lambda n}{(\lambda+\mu)n + \kappa n^2} = \frac{\lambda}{\lambda+\mu+\kappa n} \; ,$$

(124)

$$\Pr[\text{Death at } t \mid \text{Event has occurred at } t] = \frac{\mu n + \kappa n^2}{(\lambda+\mu)n + \kappa n^2} = \frac{\mu+\kappa n}{\lambda+\mu+\kappa n}$$

For μ and κ unchanged, the conditional probability of a birth increases with increasing λ, while the conditional probability of a death decreases. Starting at $X_1(0) = 1$, a high conditional probability of a birth makes it more likely to reach $X_2 = 2$ where our probability of extinction is reduced from state $X_1 = 1$. Likewise the probability of extinction is reduced for increasing X_1. Once the process increases away from zero, it is likely to approach the deterministic asymptote and oscillate about it, with of course some small probability of oscillating as far away as zero and becoming extinct. Note that the conditional probabilities (124) change not with the absolute difference of λ and μ, assuming κ is very small, but with the relative change in $(\lambda-\mu)$. For example for $\lambda = .5$, $\mu = .4$, κ very small, we have

$$\Pr[\text{Birth} \mid \text{Event}] \cong .5556,$$

$$\Pr[\text{Death} \mid \text{Event}] \cong .4444,$$

which values are unchanged for $\lambda = 5.$, $\mu = 4.$, despite the fact that the difference in $\lambda - \mu$ changes from 0.1 to 1.0. On the other hand, for $\lambda = 1.0$, $\mu = .4$, we have

$$\Pr[\text{Birth} \mid \text{Event}] \cong .7143$$

$$\Pr[\text{Death} \mid \text{Event}] \cong .2857$$

while the absolute difference $(\lambda-\mu) = .6$. One of the chief omissions of the deterministic formulation is the possibility of extinction. We would expect improved fit to the simulation if we censor early extinctions, say $t \leq 10$. Figure 10f –10g give results for the censored simulation mean ($\lambda = .5$, $\mu = .35$, $\kappa = 4.0 \times 10^{-3}$) and the non-censored case for the same parameters. As expected, the fit is improved by censoring. We conclude, then, that the approximation will work better for faster

SIMULATION MEAN VERSUS APPROXIMATE MEAN

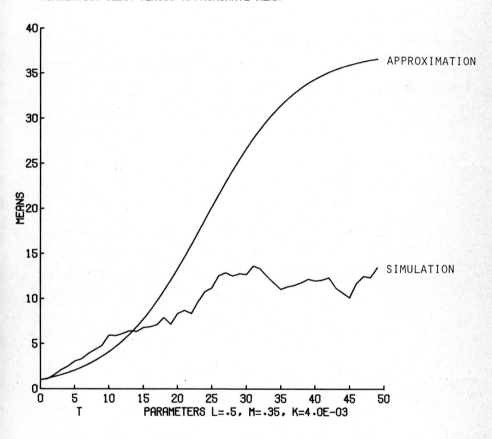

T   VERSUS AMEAN   50 VALUES
T   VERSUS XMEAN   50 VALUES

FIGURE **10f**

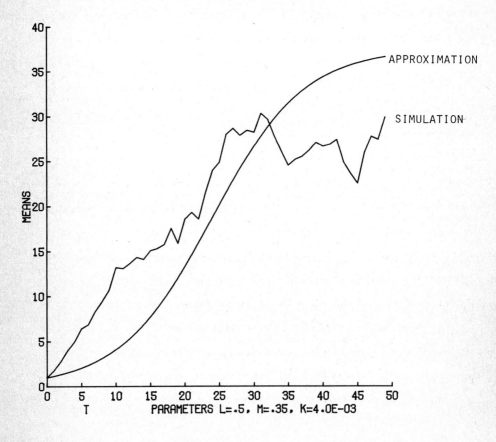

CENSORED SIMULATION MEAN VERSUS APPROXIMATE MEAN

T VERSUS AMEAN   50 VALUES
T VERSUS XMEAN   50 VALUES

FIGURE 10g

growing tumors, i.e. where the relative difference of λ and μ would be large

[assuming $\kappa \ll (\lambda-\mu)$], thus decreasing the chance of early extinction.

The simulation for $\lambda = .5$, $\mu = .35$, $\kappa = 4.0 \times 10^{-3}$, exhibits similar properties

to the hypercellularity observed by Shimkin and Polissar (1955, 1967), as discussed

in Chapter 2. Out of twenty iterations, eleven are early extinctions that remain

small and die out by $t = 10$, while the other nine exhibit eventual increases in

size toward the asymptote (see Table I). Qualitatively at least, the simulation

of the immunological feedback model duplicates Shimkin and Polissar's observation:

hypercellularity followed by the development of "killer" tumors. Thus this phenom-

enon can be explained by a one-stage feedback model, providing an alternative to

the two-stage model of Neyman and Scott.

The plots in Figure 11 certainly confirm our expectation that the approximate

variance obtained by linearizing transition probabilities is an overestimation.

The approximation diverges to infinity very quickly, while the simulation variance

does not. We have no information on the divergence or convergence of the true

variance, but certainly only an infinite number of simulations could suffice to

produce a simulation variance that diverged. The censoring procedure used for the

mean indicates nothing clearcut for the variance (see Figure 11f - 11g). The

simulation variance as compared to that from van Kampen's method is given in

Figure 13, where the latter appears to be an underestimate. The fit would be a

little better if we censored early extinctions (see Figure 11f), which reduces the

variance. This is understandable since van Kampen's method essentially assumes

that we are oscillating around an asymptote. Plots in Figure 12 indicate that the

probability of extinction obtained from the method of linearized transition proba-

bilities is an overestimate of the exact extinction probability. Examining death

transition probabilities [see (112)], we find that for $X(t) < \hat{X}(t)$, the probability

of a death occurring is greater for the approximation. Whereas the opposite is

true for $X(t) > \hat{X}(t)$, so that it is unlikely that the process will increase far

above $\hat{X}$. For values near $\hat{X}$, the death transition probabilities for the exact process

and the approximation will be nearly equal. Hence it is not unreasonable to expect

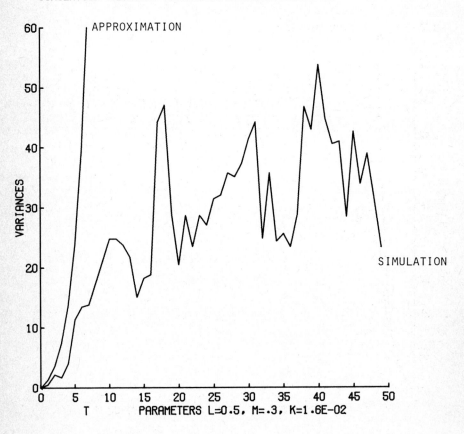

FIGURE **11a**

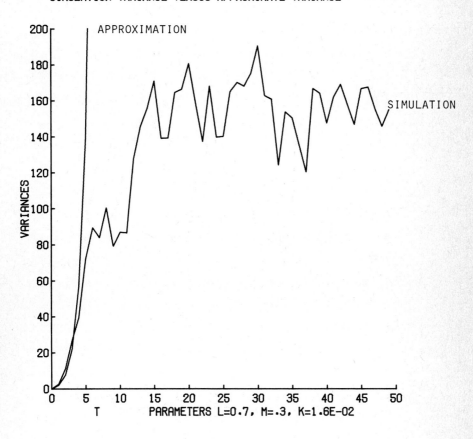

SIMULATION VARIANCE VERSUS APPROXIMATE VARIANCE

T   VERSUS XVAR   50 VALUES
T   VERSUS AVAR   50 VALUES

FIGURE 11b

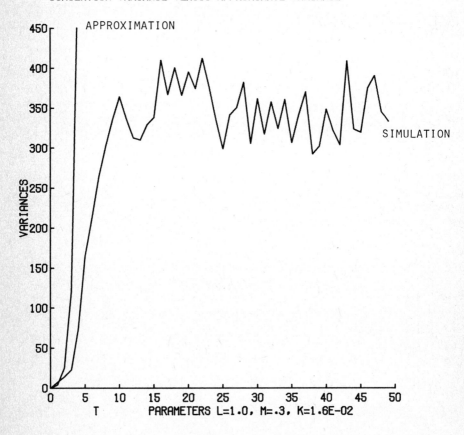

FIGURE **11c**

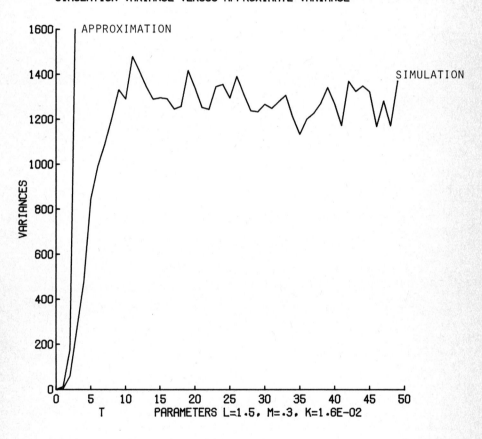

SIMULATION VARIANCE VERSUS APPROXIMATE VARIANCE

APPROXIMATION

SIMULATION

VARIANCES

T   PARAMETERS L=1.5, M=.3, K=1.6E-02

T   VERSUS XVAR   50 VALUES
T   VERSUS AVAR   50 VALUES

FIGURE 11d

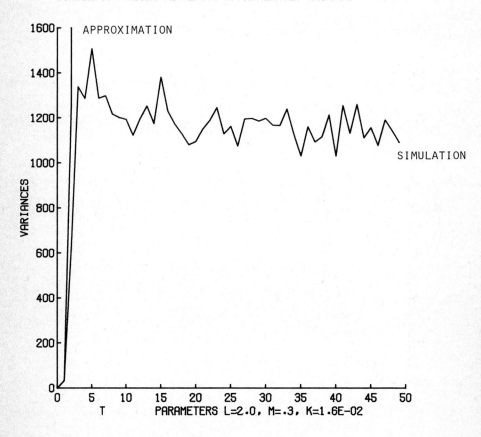

SIMULATION VARIANCE VERSUS APPROXIMATE VARIANCE

T VERSUS XVAR   50 VALUES
T VERSUS AVAR   50 VALUES

FIGURE **11e**

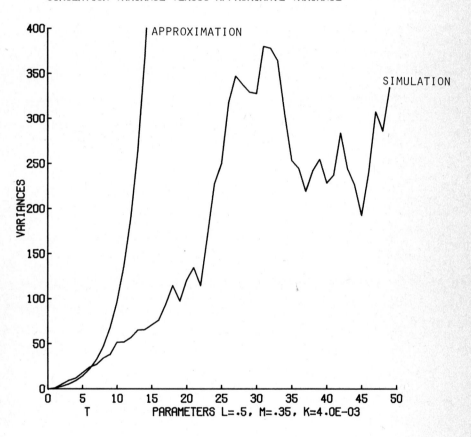

SIMULATION VARIANCE VERSUS APPROXIMATE VARIANCE

APPROXIMATION

SIMULATION

VARIANCES

PARAMETERS L=.5, M=.35, K=4.0E-03

| T | VERSUS XVAR | 50 VALUES |
| T | VERSUS AVAR | 50 VALUES |

FIGURE 11f

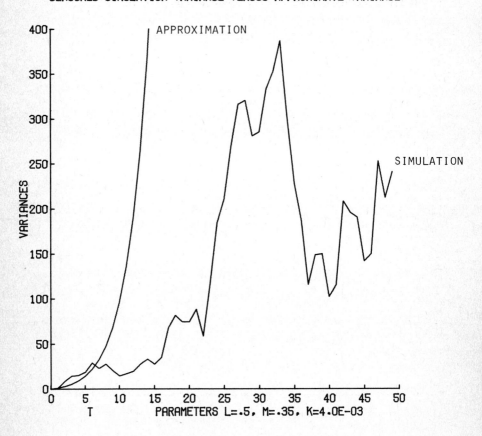

FIGURE **11g**

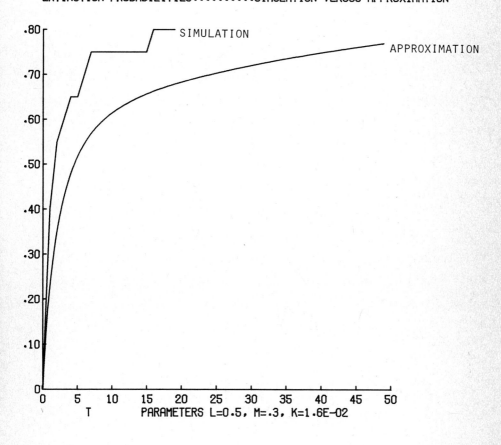

FIGURE **12a**

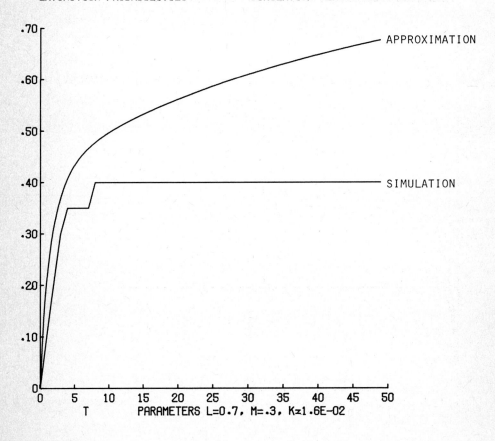

EXTINCTION PROBABILITIES.........SIMULATION VERSUS APPROXIMATION

PARAMETERS L=0.7, M=.3, K=1.6E-02

T   VERSUS PRAO   50 VALUES
T   VERSUS PRXO   50 VALUES

FIGURE **12b**

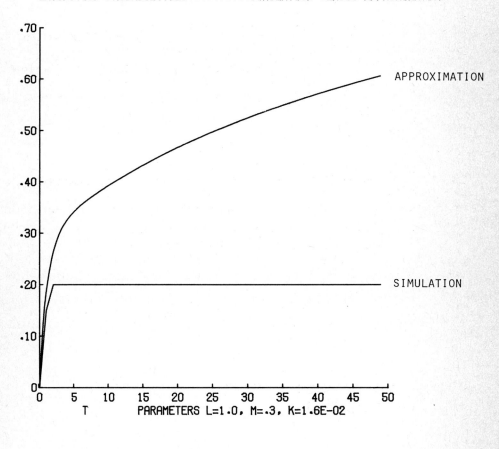

FIGURE **12c**

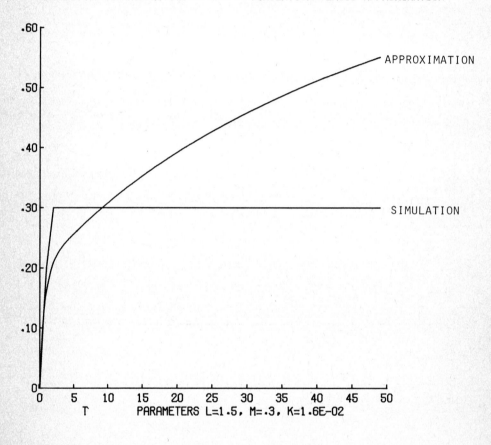

EXTINCTION PROBABILITIES..........SIMULATION VERSUS APPROXIMATION

APPROXIMATION

SIMULATION

T   PARAMETERS L=1.5, M=.3, K=1.6E-02

T VERSUS PRAO   50 VALUES
T VERSUS PRXO   50 VALUES

FIGURE **12d**

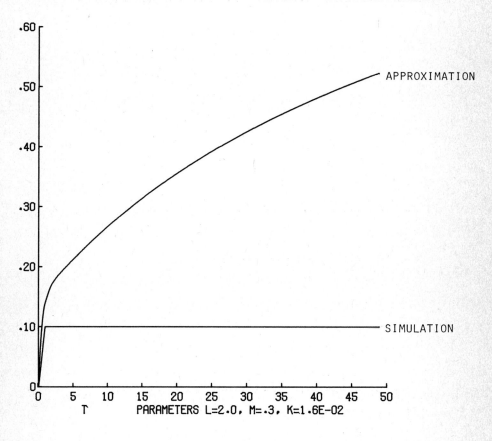

EXTINCTION PROBABILITIES.........SIMULATION VERSUS APPROXIMATION

PARAMETERS L=2.0, M=.3, K=1.6E-02

| T | VERSUS PRAO | 50 VALUES |
| T | VERSUS PRXO | 50 VALUES |

FIGURE 12e

98

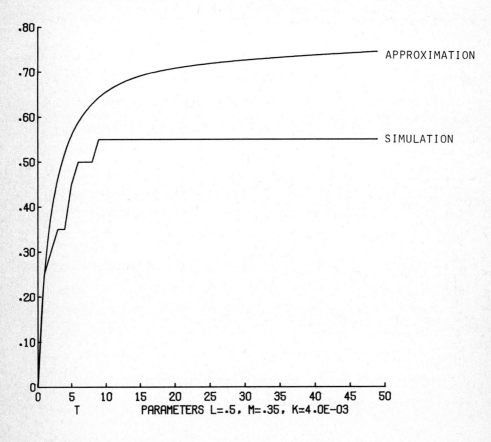

EXTINCTION PROBABILITIES.........SIMULATION VERSUS APPROXIMATION

APPROXIMATION

SIMULATION

T   PARAMETERS L=.5, M=.35, K=4.0E−03

T   VERSUS PRAO   50 VALUES
T   VERSUS PRXO   50 VALUES

FIGURE 12f

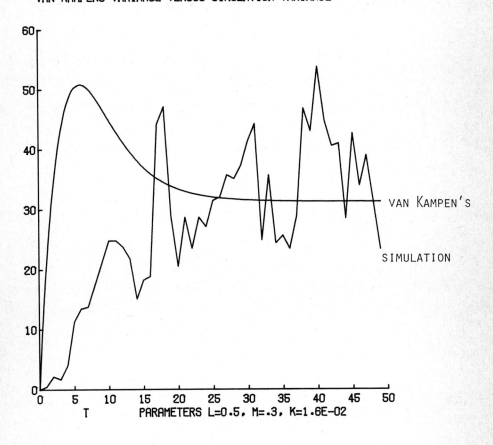

VAN KAMPENS VARIANCE VERSUS SIMULATION VARIANCE

PARAMETERS L=0.5, M=.3, K=1.6E-02

T   VERSUS XVAR   50 VALUES
T   VERSUS Y3   50 VALUES

FIGURE 13a

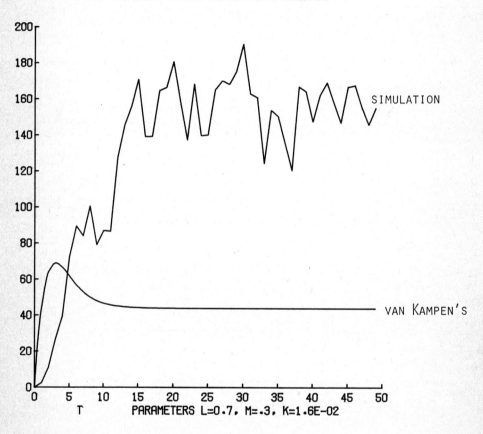

VAN KAMPENS VARIANCE VERSUS SIMULATION VARIANCE

PARAMETERS L=0.7, M=.3, K=1.6E-02

T   VERSUS XVAR   50 VALUES
T   VERSUS Y3   50 VALUES

FIGURE 13b

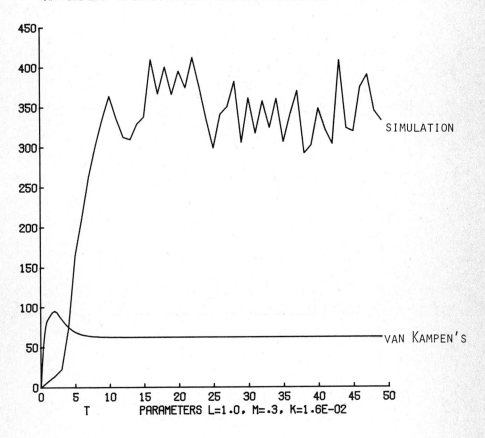

VAN KAMPENS VARIANCE VERSUS SIMULATION VARIANCE

PARAMETERS L=1.0, M=.3, K=1.6E-02

T   VERSUS XVAR   50 VALUES
T   VERSUS Y3   50 VALUES

FIGURE 13c

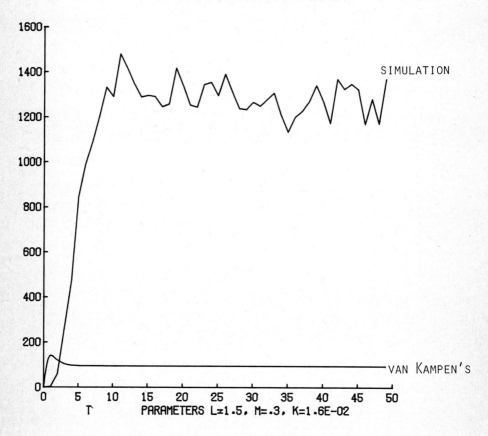

VAN KAMPENS VARIANCE VERSUS SIMULATION VARIANCE

PARAMETERS L=1.5, M=.3, K=1.6E-02

T   VERSUS XVAR   50 VALUES
T   VERSUS Y3   50 VALUES

FIGURE 13d

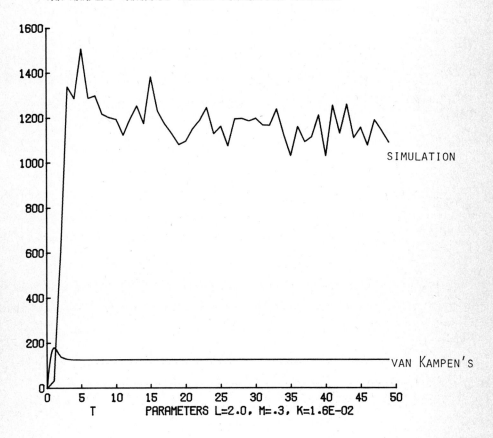

VAN KAMPENS VARIANCE VERSUS SIMULATION VARIANCE

SIMULATION

VAN KAMPEN'S

T   PARAMETERS L=2.0, M=.3, K=1.6E-02

T   VERSUS XVAR   50 VALUES
T   VERSUS Y3   50 VALUES

FIGURE **13e**

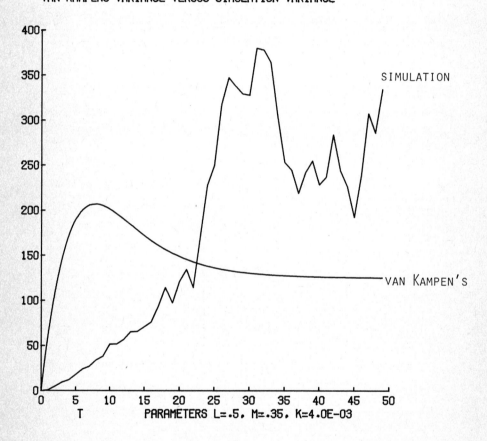

VAN KAMPENS VARIANCE VERSUS SIMULATION VARIANCE

SIMULATION

VAN KAMPEN'S

T   PARAMETERS L=.5, M=.35, K=4.0E-03

T   VERSUS XVAR   50 VALUES
T   VERSUS Y3   50 VALUES

FIGURE **13f**

105

Table 1

Values of X(t) versus t where X(t) is the size of the population at time t, from the simulation program given in Appendix III for the parameter values λ = .5, μ = .35, κ = 4x10⁻³.

t	0	5	10	15	20	25	30	35	40	45	50
	1	6	15	19	19	26	48	34	35	43	41
	1	6	7	11	15	39	42	38	34	17	29
	1	1	0	0	0	0	0	0	0	0	0
	1	2	1	0	0	0	0	0	0	0	0
	1	3	6	10	4	11	14	13	20	15	22
	1	0	0	0	0	0	0	0	0	0	0
	1	0	0	0	0	0	0	0	0	0	0
	1	0	0	0	0	0	0	0	0	0	0
	1	0	0	0	0	0	0	0	0	0	0
	1	5	18	24	25	24	31	31	34	39	41
	1	1	10	13	20	40	43	61	42	32	47
	1	2	15	6	2	12	9	7	13	15	15
	1	1	0	0	0	0	0	0	0	0	0
	1	0	0	0	0	0	0	0	0	0	0
	1	0	0	0	0	0	0	0	0	0	0
	1	13	9	17	16	14	21	18	15	10	27
	1	0	0	0	0	0	0	0	0	0	0
	1	1	0	0	0	0	0	0	0	0	0
	1	1	5	9	14	8	5	7	11	6	1
X	1.0	2.5	4.8	6.35	7.15	10.8	12.8	11.75	12.2	10.65	13.45

Values of X(t) for 20 iterations

the approximate probability of extinction to be an overestimate of its exact counterpart. It should be noted that for van Kampen's method, or any other continuous approximation, there is no natural counterpart to the probability of extinction.

The results of the various simulations generally augur well for the method of linearized transition probabilities, although those for the variance are uncertain. It was this which prompted the author to study the quadratic death process in the next chapter.

9. The Quadratic Death Process

In the last section it was not possible to determine exactly how close the approximate mean and variance come to their exact counterparts. We could, however, accomplish this for a nonlinear process that can be explicitly solved. We would then have an absolute measure of the results of the method of linearized transition probabilities.

Bartlett (1955) has found an iterative solution for the general birth process; here we find the solution for the analogous general death process. The equations for these processes can be solved because births only or deaths only are allowed, otherwise the equations have proven intractable. Let

$$\Pr[\Delta X_1(t) = -1 \,|\, X_1(t) = n] = \mu_n \Delta t + 0(\Delta t)$$

(125)

$$\Pr[\Delta X_1(t) = 0 \,|\, X_1(t) = n] = 1 - \mu_n \Delta t + 0(\Delta t)$$

where $X_1(0) = M$ with probability one. The differential difference equations can be written

$$\frac{dp_n(t)}{dt} = \mu_{n+1} p_{n+1}(t) - \mu_n p_n(t), \qquad\qquad 0 < n < M,$$

(126) $$\frac{dp_M(t)}{dt} = -\mu_M p_M(t),$$

$$\frac{dp_0(t)}{dt} = \mu_1 p_1(t),$$

where $p_n(t) = \Pr[X_1(t) = n]$. The second equation in (126) integrates to yield

(127) $$p_M = c_{M-1} e^{-\mu_M t}$$

and the initial condition $p_M(0) = 1$ implies that

(128) $c_M = 1.$

Using (127) in the first equation of (126) gives

(129) $\dfrac{dp_{M-1}(t)}{dt} = \mu_M e^{-\mu_M t} - \mu_{M-1}p_{M-1}(t).$

From this we obtain

(130) $p_{M-1} = c_{M-1}e^{-\mu_{M-1}} + \dfrac{\mu_M}{\mu_{M-1} - \mu_M}e^{-\mu_M t}.$

The initial condition $p_{M-1}(0) = 0$ implies that

(131) $c_{M-1} = \dfrac{-\mu_M}{\mu_{M-1} - \mu_M}.$

Successive steps yield the general result

(132) $p_n(t) = c_n e^{-\mu_n t} + \displaystyle\sum_{i=0}^{M-n-1} \dfrac{[\prod\limits_{j=n+1}^{M-i} \mu_j]c_{M-i}e^{-\mu_{M-i}t}}{[\prod\limits_{j=n}^{M-i-1}(\mu_j - \mu_{M-i})]}, \quad 1 \le n < M$

where c_n is defined by

$c_M = 1, \quad c_n = -\displaystyle\sum_{i=0}^{M-n-1} \dfrac{[\prod\limits_{j=n+1}^{M-i} \mu_j]c_{M-i}}{[\prod\limits_{j=n}^{M-i-1}(\mu_j - \mu_{M-i})]}.$

Proof by induction can be found in Appendix IV. The last equation in (126), together with (132) evaluated at $n = 1$, gives

(133) $\dfrac{dp_0(t)}{dt} = \mu_1 c_1 e^{-\mu_1 t} + \displaystyle\sum_{i=0}^{M-2} \dfrac{\mu_1[\prod\limits_{j=2}^{M-i} \mu_j]c_{M-i}e^{-\mu_{M-i}t}}{[\prod\limits_{j=1}^{M-i-1}(\mu_j - \mu_{M-i})]}$

which integrates to

(134) $p_0 = -c_1 e^{-\mu_1 t} + \displaystyle\sum_{i=0}^{M-2} \dfrac{[\prod\limits_{j=2}^{M-i} \mu_j](\dfrac{-c_{M-i}\mu_1}{\mu_{M-i}})e^{-\mu_{M-i}t}}{[\prod\limits_{j=1}^{M-i-1}(\mu_j - \mu_{M-i})]} + c_0.$

We know that $\lim\limits_{t\to\infty} p_0(t) = 1$, so that taking limits as $t \to \infty$ in (134) gives

(135) $c_0 = 1.$

Note that the c_i, $0 < i < m$, are displayed not explicitly but recursively. Thus our solution for the density $p_n(t)$ is nearly but not quite explicit.

A special case of the above would be the quadratic death process, i.e. $\mu_n = \mu n^2$. This quadratic term is similar to the nonlinear term in the birth and death process considered in the earlier sections. For the quadratic death process, we can substitute into equations already derived to obtain

$$p_n(t) = c_n e^{-\mu n^2 t} + \sum_{i=0}^{M-n-1} \frac{[\prod\limits_{j=n+1}^{M-i} j^2] c_{M-i} e^{-\mu(M-i)^2 t}}{[\prod\limits_{j=n}^{M-i-1} \{j^2 - (M-i)^2\}]}, \quad 0 < n < M$$

(136)

$$p_M(t) = e^{-\mu M^2 t},$$

$$p_0(t) = 1 - c_1 e^{-\mu t} - \sum_{i=0}^{M-2} \frac{[\prod\limits_{j=2}^{M-i} j^2] \frac{c_{M-i}}{(M-i)^2} e^{-\mu(M-i)^2 t}}{[\prod\limits_{j=1}^{M-i-1} \{j^2 - (M-i)^2\}]},$$

where $c_n = -\sum\limits_{i=0}^{M-n-1} \dfrac{[\prod\limits_{j=n+1}^{M-i} j^2] c_{M-i}}{[\prod\limits_{j=n}^{M-i-1} \{j^2 - (M-i)^2\}]}, \quad 0 < n < M.$

In order to obtain an approximation, $X_2(t)$, to the above by the method of linearized transition probabilities, set

(137) $\mu_n = \mu n^2 \approx \mu n \hat{X},$

where $\hat{X}$ is defined by the deterministic equation

(138) $\dfrac{d\hat{X}}{dt} = -\mu \hat{X}^2,$

which easily solves to

(139) $\hat{X} = \dfrac{M}{Mt + 1}.$

Using Bailey's (1964) notation as earlier, we have

$$(140) \quad \rho(t) = \int_0^t \frac{\mu M}{\mu MT + 1} \, dT$$

$$= \log(\mu Mt + 1),$$

and

$$e^{\rho(t)} = \mu Mt + 1,$$

so that the probability generating function,

$$P(z,t) = [1 + \frac{(z-1)}{\mu Mt + 1}]^M$$

(141)

$$= [\frac{z}{\mu Mt + 1} + \frac{\mu Mt}{\mu Mt + 1}]^M,$$

which is a Binomial distribution. Clearly the boundary condition of the exact process, $P(z,0) = z^M$, and the stationary distribution of the exact process,

$$\lim_{t \to \infty} P(z,t) = 1$$

will be satisfied by the approximation. Note that we know the stationary distribution of the exact process by analogous reasoning to that applied in Chapter 4. Since the approximation is Binomial (M, $\frac{1}{\mu Mt + 1}$), we can write immediately

$$c_1^{X_2}(t) = \frac{M}{\mu Mt + 1},$$

$$(142) \quad c_2^{X_2}(t) = \frac{\mu M^2 t}{(\mu Mt + 1)^2},$$

$$q_n(t) = \binom{M}{n} (\mu Mt + 1)^{-n} (\frac{\mu Mt}{\mu Mt + 1})^{M-n},$$

where $q_n(t) = \Pr[X_2(t) = n]$

That the mean of the approximation will be equal to the solution of the deterministic equation is of course guaranteed by the theorem in the preceding chapter. Because of the complicated nature of the exact solution as given in (136), it was necessary to appeal to the computer to obtain the exact mean and variance in such a form that we can compare them to the approximation. The iterative routine given in Appendix V gave the following results: plots for the stochastic means (Figure 14) and the stochastic variances (Figure 15) indicate quite a good fit; although the approximation provides overestimates, the discrepancy is only considerable for a small range of values of the variance, and the general form of the exact process is preserved. The approximation improves as μ gets smaller.

It is possible to say something about the asymptotic convergence of the approximate mean, $c_1^{X_2}$, to X_1. We write

$$(143) \quad E_{X_1}[X_1 - c_1^{X_2}]^2 = \sum_{n=0}^{M} [n - c_1^{X_2}]^2 p_n(t)$$

$$= [\frac{-\mu}{\mu Mt + 1}]^2 p_0(t) + \sum_{n=1}^{M} [n - \frac{\mu}{\mu Mt + 1}]^2 p_n(t)$$

From (136) we know that

$$\lim_{t \to \infty} p_n(t) = 0, \quad 0 < n \leq M,$$

$$(144)$$

$$\lim_{t \to \infty} p_0(t) = 1,$$

and also that

$$\lim_{t \to \infty} [\frac{-\mu}{\mu Mt + 1}]^2 = 0.$$

Hence

$$(145) \quad \lim_{\to \infty} E_{X_1}[X_1 - c_1^{X_2}]^2 = 0.$$

Thus the stochastic process $X_1(t)$ converges in quadratic mean to the approximate stochastic mean, $c_1^{X_2}$, obtained by the method of linearized transition probabilities.

For the quadratic death process we can compare $\hat{E}(\Delta)$ to the exact $E(\Delta)$ [see equations (116 - 118)], where the latter is obtained from the iterative scheme in Appendix V. We have

$$\Delta = \mu n^2 - \mu n \hat{X},$$

$$(146) \quad E(\Delta) = \mu c_2^{X_1}(t) + \mu c_1^{X_1}(t)[c_1^{X_1}(t) - \hat{X}(t)],$$

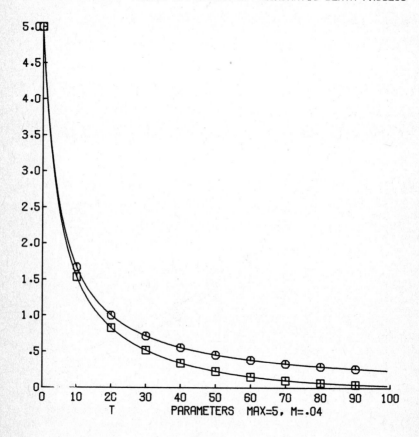

MEANS...EXACT VERSUS APPROXIMATE...QUADRATIC DEATH PROCESS

⊡ S VERSUS EXMEAN   100 VALUES   ⊡: EXACT
⊙ S VERSUS APMEAN   100 VALUES   ⊙: APPROXIMATE

FIGURE **14a**

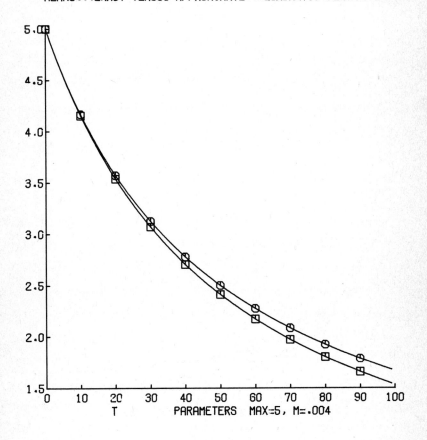

MEANS...EXACT VERSUS APPROXIMATE...QUADRATIC DEATH PROCESS

S VERSUS EXMEAN   100 VALUES   □ : EXACT
S VERSUS APMEAN   100 VALUES   ○ : APPROXIMATE

FIGURE **14b**

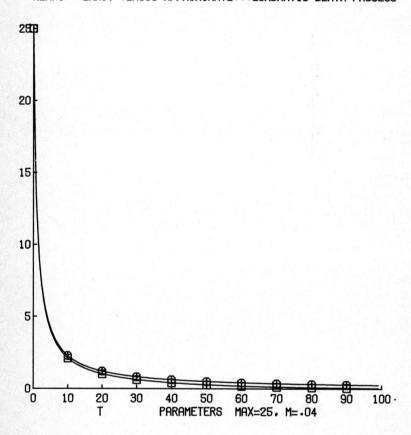

MEANS...EXACT VERSUS APPROXIMATE...QUADRATIC DEATH PROCESS

⊡ S VERSUS EXMEAN   100 VALUES   ▫ : EXACT
⦿ S VERSUS APMEAN   100 VALUES   ○ : APPROXIMATE

FIGURE **14c**

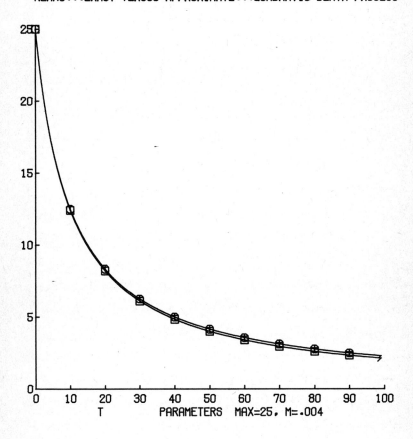

MEANS...EXACT VERSUS APPROXIMATE...QUADRATIC DEATH PROCESS

☐ S VERSUS EXMEAN   100 VALUES   ☐: EXACT

⊙ S VERSUS APMEAN   100 VALUES   o: APPROXIMATE

FIGURE **14d**

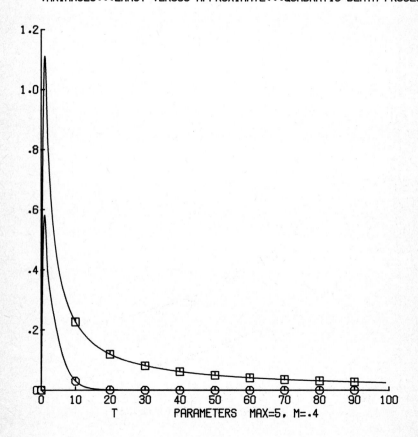

VARIANCES...EXACT VERSUS APPROXIMATE...QUADRATIC DEATH PROCESS

⊡ S VERSUS APVAR   100 VALUES   □ : APPROXIMATE
⊙ S VERSUS EXVAR   100 VALUES   ○ : EXACT

FIGURE **15a**

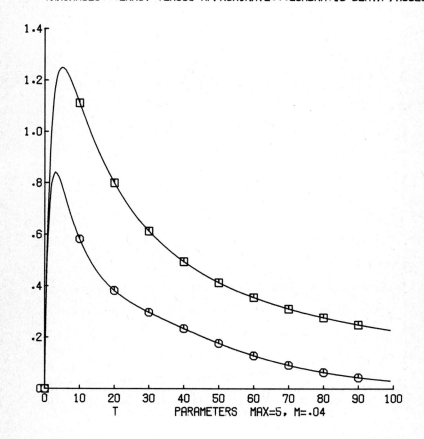

VARIANCES...EXACT VERSUS APPROXIMATE...QUADRATIC DEATH PROCESS

⊡ S VERSUS APVAR   100 VALUES   ◻: APPROXIMATE
⊕ S VERSUS EXVAR   100 VALUES   ○: EXACT

FIGURE **15b**

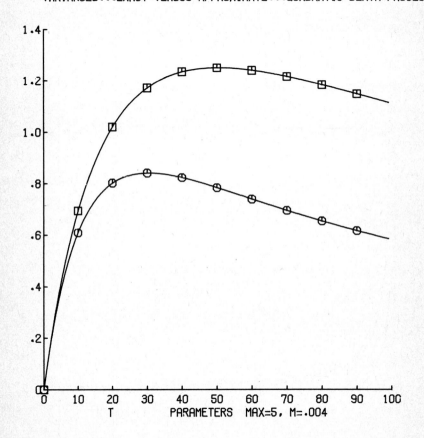

VARIANCES...EXACT VERSUS APPROXIMATE...QUADRATIC DEATH PROCESS

□ S VERSUS APVAR   100 VALUES   □ : APPROXIMATE
⊙ S VERSUS EXVAR   100 VALUES   ⊙ : EXACT

FIGURE 15c

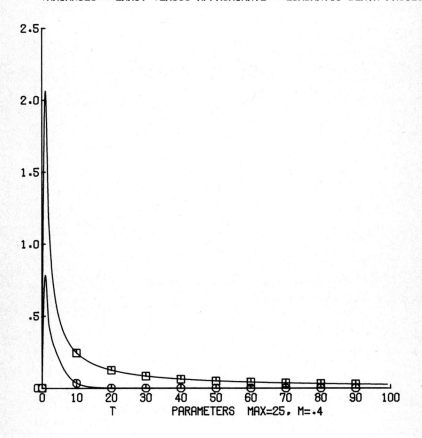

VARIANCES...EXACT VERSUS APPROXIMATE...QUADRATIC DEATH PROCESS

| ☐ | S | VERSUS APVAR | 100 VALUES | ☐ : | APPROXIMATE |
| ⊙ | S | VERSUS EXVAR | 100 VALUES | ○ : | EXACT |

FIGURE **15d**

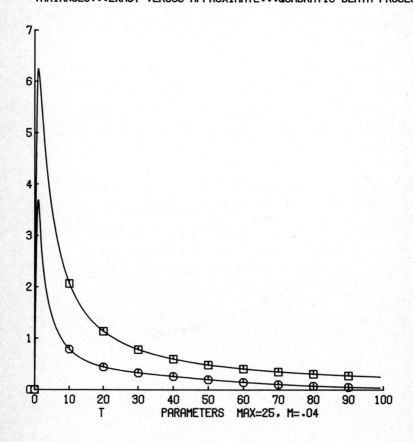

VARIANCES...EXACT VERSUS APPROXIMATE...QUADRATIC DEATH PROCESS

PARAMETERS MAX=25, M=.04

⊡ S VERSUS APVAR   100 VALUES   □ : APPROXIMATE
⊙ S VERSUS EXVAR   100 VALUES   ○ : EXACT

FIGURE **15e**

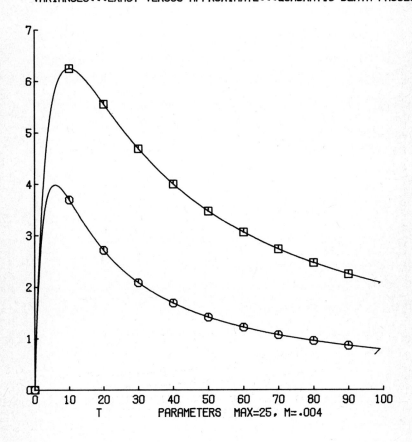

VARIANCES...EXACT VERSUS APPROXIMATE...QUADRATIC DEATH PROCESS

| ⊡ | S | VERSUS APVAR | 100 VALUES | □ : | APPROXIMATE |
| ⊙ | S | VERSUS EXVAR | 100 VALUES | ○ : | EXACT |

FIGURE **15f**

$$\hat{E}(\Delta) = \mu c_2^{X_2}(t).$$

The last equation of (146) together with (142) yields

$$(147) \quad \hat{E}(\Delta) = \frac{\mu^2 M^2 t}{(\mu M t + 1)^2} \; .$$

Now

$$(148) \quad \lim_{t \to \infty} \hat{E}(\Delta) = 0,$$

which is clearly an improvement over the result (118) for the more complicated

birth and death process considered in earlier chapters. From Figure 16 we see that

$\hat{E}(\Delta)$ is consistently a slight overestimate of the error $E(\Delta)$, and both decrease

with decreasing μ.

Figure 17 demonstrates that the approximate probability of extinction converges

to one more slowly than its exact counterpart, but again the approximation gives

good results. Although initially the approximation is greater, its rate of

increase slows and it is overtaken by the exact probability of extinction.

The agreement of results for the exact and approximate processes enables us to

use the approximation to gain understanding into the nature of the exact process,

which is of complicated form and its moments are not readily available. The approx-

imation, however, has a binomial distribution, for which we not only immediately

can write down the moments and probability density, but also a clear picture of how

the approximation behaves, without the benefit of a complicated iterative routine

on the computer.

It is tempting to extrapolate the above results for the approximation by

linearized transition probabilities in the case of the quadratic death process to

the more complicated birth and death process in our immunological feedback model.

We cannot demonstrate the theoretical results for the latter that we can for the

former, e.g. the convergence in quadratic mean [(103), (145)] or the convergence

to zero of the expected error [(118), (148)]. Neither does our nonlinear model for

births and deaths exhibit the well-behaved properties of the simpler process, such

as boundedness and the monotonicity, which enables us to solve the difference

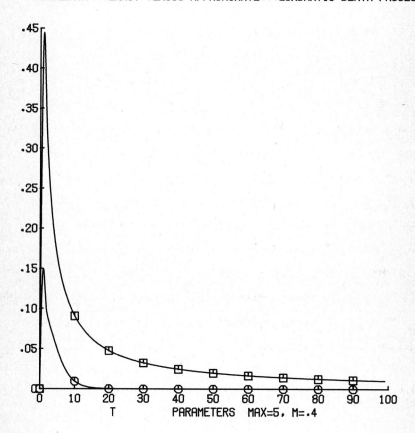

E(DELTA)...EXACT VERSUS APPROXIMATE...QUADRATIC DEATH PROCESS

⊡ S VERSUS APEDEL   100 VALUES   □: APPROXIMATE
⊙ S VERSUS EDELT   100 VALUES   ○: EXACT

FIGURE **16a**

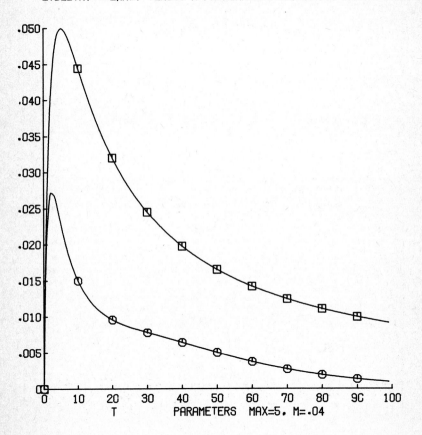

E(DELTA)...EXACT VERSUS APPROXIMATE...QUADRATIC DEATH PROCESS

□ S VERSUS APEDEL   100 VALUES   □ : APPROXIMATE
Ⓞ S VERSUS EDELT   100 VALUES   O : EXACT

FIGURE **16b**

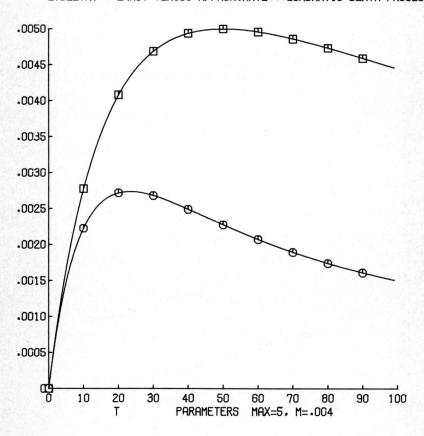

E(DELTA)...EXACT VERSUS APPROXIMATE...QUADRATIC DEATH PROCESS

PARAMETERS MAX=5, M=.004

⊡ S VERSUS APEDEL   100 VALUES   ⊡ : APPROXIMATE

⊙ S VERSUS EDELT   100 VALUES   ⊙ : EXACT

FIGURE **16c**

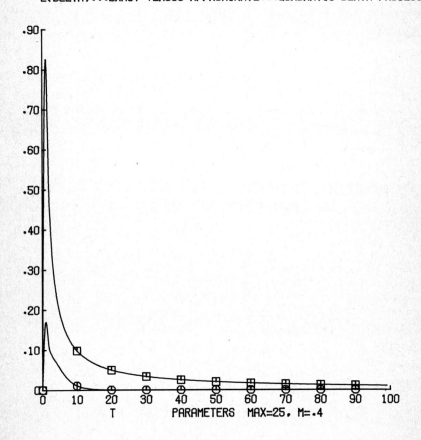

FIGURE **16d**

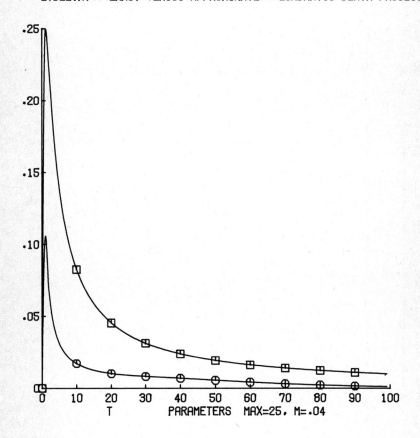

E(DELTA)...EXACT VERSUS APPROXIMATE...QUADRATIC DEATH PROCESS

⊡ S VERSUS APEDEL   100 VALUES   □ :   APPROXIMATE

⊙ S VERSUS EDELT   100 VALUES   o :   EXACT

FIGURE **16e**

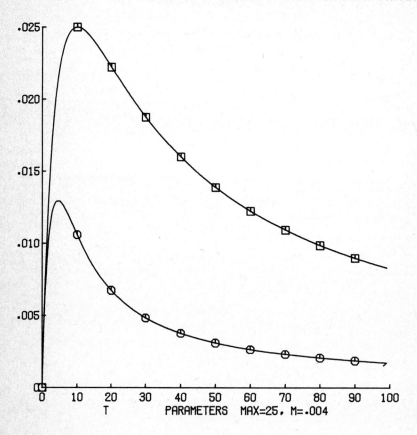

E(DELTA)...EXACT VERSUS APPROXIMATE...QUADRATIC DEATH PROCESS

☐ S VERSUS APEDEL   100 VALUES   ☐: APPROXIMATE

◎ S VERSUS EDELT   100 VALUES   ○: EXACT

FIGURE **16f**

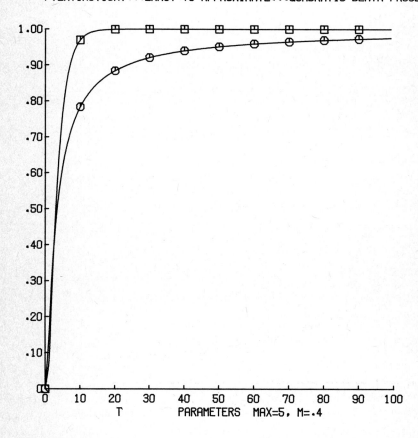

P(EXTINCTION)...EXACT VS APPROXIMATE...QUADRATIC DEATH PROCESS

T   PARAMETERS MAX=5, M=.4

▣ S VERSUS PRXO   100 VALUES   □ :   EXACT

⊙ S VERSUS PRAO   100 VALUES   ○ :   APPROXIMATE

FIGURE **17a**

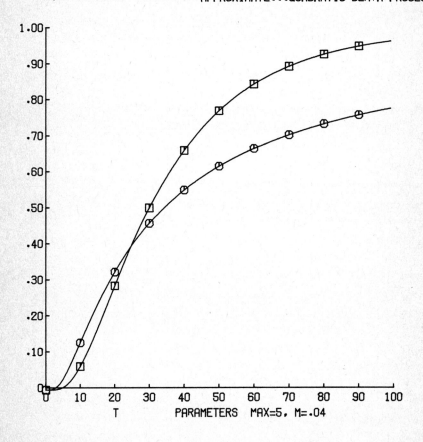

P(EXTINCTION)...EXACT VS APPROXIMATE...QUADRATIC DEATH PROCESS

PARAMETERS MAX=5, M=.04

☐ S VERSUS PRXO   100 VALUES   ☐ : EXACT
Ⓞ S VERSUS PRAO   100 VALUES   O : APPROXIMATE

FIGURE **17b**

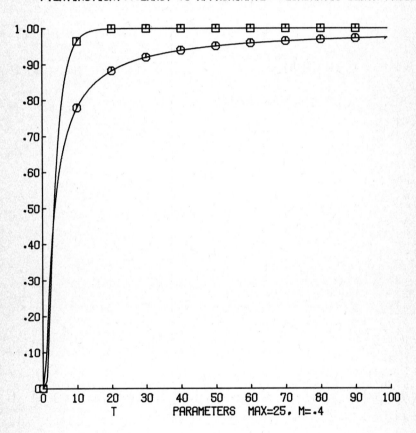

P(EXTINCTION)...EXACT VS APPROXIMATE...QUADRATIC DEATH PROCESS

☐ S VERSUS PRXO   100 VALUES   ☐ : EXACT

⊙ S VERSUS PRAO   100 VALUES   ⊙ : APPROXIMATE

FIGURE **17c**

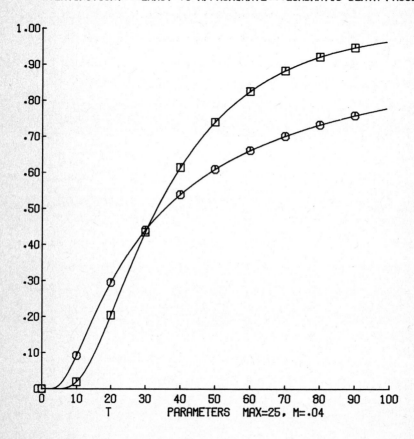

P(EXTINCTION)...EXACT VS APPROXIMATE...QUADRATIC DEATH PROCESS

PARAMETERS MAX=25, M=.04

☐ S VERSUS PRXO   100 VALUES   ☐: EXACT
Ⓞ S VERSUS PRAO   100 VALUES   ⊙: APPROXIMATE

FIGURE **17d**

equation in the first place. Nor do the limits as t→∞ of the mean and variance of
the latter process equal the mean and variance of its stationary distribution,
which relationships hold for the former process. Nevertheless, the quadratic death
process corresponds to the nonlinear part of the transition probabilities for the
immunological feedback model, and, further, results for the quadratic death process
confirm that the approximate mean, variance, and $E(\Delta)$ obtained by the method of
linearized transition probabilities are consistently overestimates. The approximation works best here for small μ, which correspond to the small $\kappa [<< (\lambda-\mu)]$ we
would consider for tumors that grow to be very large.

10. The Collective Model

The bulk of the aforegoing research has been concerned with deriving and evaluating approximations to the stochastic model for a single tumor, whereas in Chapter 4 we originally presented a model for collective tumor growth, i.e., the growth of (possibly) many tumors in a single tissue, under a Poisson rate of initiation given in the first equation of (1). Here we derive some properties of the collective model and discuss the complexities of its solution.

$$(149) \quad \frac{d\hat{X}}{dt} = D(t) + (\lambda-\mu)\hat{X} - \kappa\hat{X}^2.$$

Under the assumption that $D(t) = D$, a constant rate of mutation, we have

$$(150) \quad \frac{d\hat{X}}{dt} = D + (\lambda-\mu)\hat{X} - \kappa\hat{X}^2.$$

This can be rewritten as

$$(151) \quad \frac{d\hat{X}}{D + (\lambda-\mu)\hat{X} - \kappa\hat{X}^2} = \frac{dt}{1},$$

which becomes, since

$$(152) \quad \frac{1}{D + (\lambda-\mu)\hat{X} - \kappa\hat{X}} = \frac{1}{d(\frac{\lambda-\mu+d}{2\kappa} - \hat{X})} - \frac{1}{d(\frac{\lambda-\mu-d}{2} - \hat{X})},$$

where $d = [(\lambda-\mu)^2 + 4D\kappa]^{\frac{1}{2}}$ and noting that $\hat{X} > (\lambda-\mu-d)/2\kappa$ since $x > 0$,

$$(153) \quad \frac{dx}{d(\frac{\lambda-\mu+d}{2\kappa} - \hat{X})} + \frac{dx}{d(\hat{X} - \frac{\lambda-\mu-d}{2\kappa})} = \frac{dt}{1}.$$

Integrating we obtain

$$(154) \quad \frac{\hat{X} - \frac{(\lambda-\mu-d)}{2\kappa}}{\frac{(\lambda-\mu+d)}{2\kappa} - \hat{X}} = c_1 e^{dt},$$

where c_1 is to be determined from initial conditions. Since $\hat{X}(0) = 0$, we have

$$(155) \quad c_1 = \frac{d - (\lambda-\mu)}{d + (\lambda-\mu)} > 0.$$

After some algebraic manipulation, we have

$$(156) \quad \hat{X}(t) = [\frac{d + (\lambda-\mu)}{2\kappa}]\frac{(e^{dt} - 1)}{(e^{dt} + \frac{1}{c_1})} \cdot$$

Now

$$(157) \quad \frac{d\hat{X}}{dt} = \frac{c_1 d^2 e^{dt}}{\kappa(1 + c_1 e^{dt})^2} > 0,$$

so that $\hat{X}$ is always increasing. Further

$$(158) \quad \lim_{t\to\infty} \hat{X}(t) = \frac{d + (\lambda-\mu)}{2\kappa}$$

is its asymptotic upper limit. The form of this equation is similar to the logistic, as is demonstrated by Figure 18.

The stationary distribution for the collective model can be found, but is not of so simple a form as the single tumor model. Recall that because the latter has an absorbing barrier at $X = 0$, the only stationary distribution is degenerate at $X = 0$. So long as $D(t) = D > 0$, the collective model lacks this absorbing barrier; hence it has a non-trivial stationary distribution. We write the forward Kolmogorov equations:

$$\frac{dp_n(t)}{dt} = [D + \lambda(n-1)]p_{n-1}(t) - [D + (\lambda+\mu+\kappa n)n]p_n(t)$$

$$(159) \qquad\qquad + [\mu+\kappa(n+1)](n+1)p_{n+1}(t), \qquad n \geq 1,$$

$$\frac{dp_0(t)}{dt} = -Dp_0(t) + (\mu+\kappa)p_1(t).$$

We set $\dfrac{dp_i(t)}{dt} = 0$ for all i to obtain the stationary distribution. Equations (159) can then be rewritten

$$p_1 = \frac{D}{\mu + \kappa} p_0,$$

$$p_2 = \frac{D + \lambda}{2(\mu + 2\kappa)} p_1,$$

$$(160)$$

$$p_3 = \frac{D + 2\lambda}{3(\mu + 3\kappa)} p_2,$$

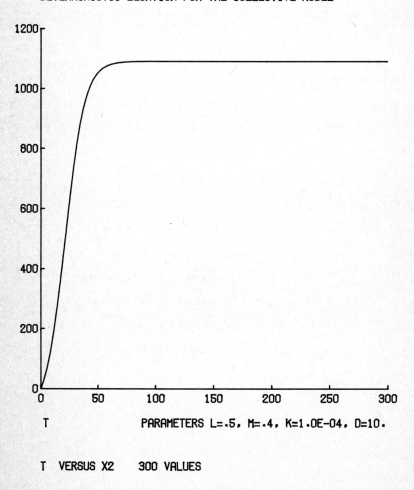

DETERMINISTIC EQUATION FOR THE COLLECTIVE MODEL

T   PARAMETERS L=.5, M=.4, K=1.0E-04, D=10.

T   VERSUS X2   300 VALUES

FIGURE **18**

$$\vdots$$

$$p_n = \frac{D + (n-1)\lambda}{n(\mu + \kappa n)} \, p_{n-1},$$

or equivalently

$$(161) \quad p_n = \frac{\displaystyle\prod_{i=0}^{n-1} (D + \lambda i)}{\displaystyle n! \prod_{j=1}^{n} (\mu + \kappa j)} \, p_0$$

where p_0 is chosen so that $\displaystyle\sum_{n=0}^{\infty} p_n = 1$. We have

$$\lim_{n\to\infty} \left| \frac{p_{n+1}}{p_n} \right| = \lim_{n\to\infty} \frac{\left(\frac{D}{n} + \lambda\right)}{\left(1 + \frac{1}{n}\right)} \cdot \frac{1}{[\mu + \kappa(n+1)]} = 0$$

which means $\displaystyle\sum_{n=0}^{\infty} p_n$ converges absolutely.

If we try to obtain an approximation to the collective model by the method of linearized transition probabilities, we find it would be necessary to solve a nonhomogeneous birth and death process with immigration. This stochastic process does not yield to easy solution under the general conditions for the process without immigration, although the generalizations of the theorem in Chapter 8 apply. However, it is possible to find the stationary distribution for the now "linearized" analogue of equations (159),

$$\frac{dq_n(t)}{dt} = [D + \lambda(n-1)]q_{n-1}(t) - [D + \{\lambda+\mu+\kappa\hat{X}(t)\}n]q_n(t)$$

$$(162) \qquad\qquad + [\mu + \kappa\hat{X}(t)](n+1)q_{n+1}(t), \qquad n \geq 1,$$

$$\frac{dq_0(t)}{dt} = -Dq_0(t) + [\mu + \kappa\hat{X}(t)]q_1(t),$$

where $\hat{X}$ satisfies equation (156). As before we set $dq_i/dt = 0$ for all i and

$$\hat{X}(t) + \frac{d + (\lambda - \mu)}{2\kappa}$$

we obtain

$$q_1 = \frac{D}{\mu + \kappa\hat{X}} q_0,$$

(163)
$$q_2 = \frac{D + \lambda}{2(\mu + \kappa\hat{X})} q_1,$$

.
.
.

$$q_n = \frac{D + (n-1)\lambda}{n(\mu + \kappa\hat{X})} q_{n-1},$$

which implies

$$q_n = \frac{\prod\limits_{i=0}^{n-1} (D + \lambda i)}{n!(\mu + \kappa\hat{X})^n} q_0,$$

(164)

$$= \frac{\prod\limits_{i=0}^{n-1} (D + \lambda i)}{n!(\frac{d+\lambda+\mu}{2})^n} q_0,$$

where q_0 is chosen so that $\sum\limits_{n=0}^{\infty} q_n = 1$. Now

(165) $\lim\limits_{n \to \infty} \left| \frac{q_{n+1}}{q_n} \right| = \lim\limits_{n \to \infty} \frac{(D + \lambda n)}{(n+1)(\frac{d+\lambda+\mu}{2})}$

$$= \frac{2\lambda}{d + \lambda + \mu}$$

Since $d > \lambda - \mu$ implies $d + \lambda + \mu > 2\lambda$, we have

$$\frac{2\lambda}{d + \lambda + \mu} < 1;$$

hence $\sum\limits_{n=0}^{\infty} q_n$ converges absolutely. Thus, we see that, unlike the case for process without immigration, i.e., the single tumor model, the stationary distribution of the approximation here does not coincide with the stationary distribution of the exact process. It is of interest to ascertain whether the stochastic mean of the approximation coincides with the solution of the deterministic equation of the collective model. Note that, since we have changed the single tumor model only by the addition of an "immigration" component in the transition probability for birth corresponding to the initiation of new tumor clones by mutation, the theorem we have already proven guarantees that the mean of the approximation satisfies the deterministic equation. We need only apply the theorem for

$$(166) \quad a_0 = D, \; \lambda(t) = \lambda, \; b_0 = 0, \; \mu(t) = \mu + \kappa \hat{X}(t).$$

11. Further Implications of the Immunological Feedback Model

Neyman and Scott (1967) were able to derive, for their model, expressions for the probability that a tumor will be counted by the experimenter and the expected number of so-called "killer" tumors. Although it is not explicitly stated, Neyman and Scott appear to make the implicit assumption that, once a tumor is counted, it grows without limit and is classified as a killer tumor. Analogously, we derive the above quantities for the immunological feedback model, but where we use the probability density obtained from the method of linearized transition probabilities instead of the unavailable exact density.

Following Neyman and Scott, we let

$$(167) \quad \pi_n = \Pr[\text{A tumor of size n cells will be counted}] = \sum_{i=0}^{n-1} a_i$$

where the a_i are arbitrary but non-negative and

$$\sum_{i=0}^{\infty} a_i = 1.$$

It seems reasonable that π_n is an increasing function of n and $\pi_n \to 1$ as $n \to \infty$. Further let

$$(168) \quad \pi(t) = \Pr[\text{A tumor of age t will be counted}] = \sum_{n=1}^{\infty} p_n(t)\pi_n,$$

where $p_n(t)$ satisfies equations (97),

$$= \frac{(\lambda-\mu)}{h(t)}[1 - \frac{h_2(t)}{h(t)}] \sum_{n=1}^{\infty} [\frac{h_2(t)}{h(t)}]^{n-1} \sum_{\kappa=0}^{n-1} a_\kappa,$$

$$= \phi(t)[1 - R(t)] \sum_{n=1}^{\infty} [R(t)]^{n-1} \sum_{\kappa=0}^{n-1} a_\kappa$$

where $\phi(t) = (\lambda-\mu)/h(t)$, $R(t) = h_2(t)/h(t)$,

$$= \phi(t)[1 - R(t)] \cdot \frac{1}{[1 - R(t)]} \sum_{\kappa=0}^{\infty} a_\kappa R^\kappa$$

$$(169)$$

$$= \phi(t)g[R(t)]$$

where $g(x) = \sum\limits_{\kappa=0}^{\infty} a_\kappa x^\kappa$. Now

$$\lim_{t\to\infty} h(t) = +\infty,$$

(170)
$$\lim_{t\to\infty} \frac{h_2(t)}{h(t)} = 1,$$

so that

$$\lim_{t\to\infty} \phi(t) = 0,$$

(171)
$$\lim_{t\to\infty} R(t) = 1.$$

Since $\sum\limits_{\kappa=0}^{\infty} a_\kappa = 1$, we have

(172) $\lim\limits_{t\to\infty} g[R(t)] = 1.$

Hence

(173) $\lim\limits_{t\to\infty} \Pi(t) = 0.$

This is consistent with the stationary distribution, which tells us that all tumors of age $t = +\infty$ will be extinct.

For $0 < t \leq T$, let $z(t,T)$ be the number of tumors generated in $[0,t)$ and counted at T, under the Poisson rate of initiation $D(t)$. Further let

(174) $q_n(t) = Pr[z(t,T) = n].$

At this point Neyman and Scott implicitly assume that, once a tumor is large enough to be counted, it remains large enough to be counted. Clearly this is not exactly so, since there is always the possibility that a tumor will decrease to a smaller size. Under that assumption, however, we can write

(175) $q_n(t + \Delta t) = q_{n-1}(t)D(t)\Pi(T - t)\Delta t + q_n(t)[1 - D(t)\Pi(T - t)\Delta t] + O(\Delta t),$

which means $z(t,T)$ is a Poisson variable with expectation

(176) $\xi(t,T) = \int\limits_0^t D(x)\Pi(T-x)dx.$

For $t = T$, we have

(177) $\quad \xi(T) = \int_0^T D(x)\Pi(T-x)dx.$

This together with (205) tells us that

(178) $\quad \lim_{T\to\infty} \xi(T) = 0.$

Thus the expected number of killer tumors is zero. At face value, this might seem disastrous for the immunological feedback model. After all, the probability of a tumor developing and killing its host is certainly greater than zero. The difficulty arises because we let $t \to \infty$ consider a killer tumor as one that grows without limit. In practice t will be finite, so that it is appropriate to consider not the asymptotic distribution but rather the distribution after some finite t. This is especially important for the immumological feedback model since the asymptotic distribution is radically different from the distribution at finite but large t. And certainly it is reasonable to assume that when a tumor reaches a certain size (possibly random), the host organism dies. Thus it would be appropriate to consider the number of tumors generated in $[0,t)$ greater than or equal to size w at some finite $t = T$, where w is a random variable such that when $X(t) > w$, the host dies. Call this $z^*(t,T)$. Further define

(179) $\quad \Pi^*(t) = \Pr[X(t) \geq w],$

$$= \int_{w_o} \Pr[X(t) \geq w | w = w_o]\Pr[w = w_o]dw_o,$$

$$= \int_{w_o} \sum_{n=w_o}^{\infty} p_n(t)g(w_o)dw_o,$$

where g is the density of w. Using the approximation (97) and assuming that $w = w_o$ with probability one,

$$\Pi^*(t) = \sum_{n=w_o}^{\infty} \frac{(\lambda-\mu)}{h(t)} [1 - \frac{h_2(t)}{h(t)}][\frac{h_2(t)}{h(t)}]^{n-1},$$

$$(180) \qquad = [\frac{h_2(t)}{h(t)}]^{w_o-1} \sum_{n=1}^{\infty} \frac{(\lambda-\mu)}{h(t)} [1 - \frac{h_2(t)}{h(t)}][\frac{h_2(t)}{h(t)}]^{n-1},$$

$$= [\frac{h_2(t)}{h(t)}]^{w_o-1} \cdot \frac{(\lambda-\mu)}{h(t)}$$

Let $q_n^*(t) = Pr[z^*(t,T) = n]$, then by reasoning analogous to that of Neyman and Scott applied to z gives

$$(181) \quad q_n^*(t + \Delta t) = q_{n-1}^*(t)D(t)\Pi^*(T-t)\Delta t + q_n^*(t)[1 - D(t)\Pi^*(T-t)\Delta t] + 0(\Delta t),$$

which means z* is a Poisson variable with expectation

$$(182) \quad \xi^*(t,T) = \int_0^t D(x)\Pi^*(T-x)dx.$$

Letting $t = T$, we have

$$\xi^*(T) = \int_0^T D(x)\Pi^*(T-x)dx,$$

$$(183)$$

$$= \int_0^T D(x)[\frac{h_2(T-x)}{h(T-x)}]^{(w_o-1)} \cdot \frac{(\lambda-\mu)}{h(T-x)} dx.$$

It is not possible to further evaluate (187) without specifying $D(x)$. Suppose we let $D(x) = D$, a constant, then

$$\xi^*(T) = D\int_0^T [\frac{h_2(T-x)}{h(T-x)}]^{w_o} dx,$$

$$(184)$$

$$= D\int_0^T [1 + \frac{\{(\lambda-\mu-\kappa)e^{(\lambda-\mu)(x-T)} + \kappa\}}{\{\frac{\lambda(\lambda-\mu-\kappa)}{(\lambda-\mu)}\left\{1 - e^{(\lambda-\mu)(x-T)}\right\} + \lambda\kappa(T-x)\}}]^{-w_o} dx.$$

An explicit solution of this integral is not available, but a numerical solution could be obtained for specific values of λ,μ,κ,T, and w_o.

The immunological response mechanism we have hypothesized is fundamentally of simple form and, despite mathematical complexities, one ought to think about the incorporation of additional biological ideas. For instance, since it is known that tumors are composed of dead as well as living cells, we could examine the cumulative population of the stochastic process (2), i.e. the total number of tumor cells, living and dead. This entails solution of the two dimensional stochastic process $[X(t),Z(t)]$ where $X(t)$ is the number of living tumor cells and $Z(t)$ is the cumulative population. Alternatively, since the feedback response may depend on the size of the population at some previous time or over a range of times, we might alter the transition probabilities in the linearizing method of the same by replacing $\hat{X}(t)$ with $\hat{X}(t-1)$, $\hat{X}(t-c)$, or indeed

$$\frac{1}{b-a} \int_a^b \hat{X}(t)dt.$$

Another possibility is a spatial consideration: perhaps cells interior to a tumor are not subject to as high a probability of immunological response, being somehow protected by the outer cells, a kind of reverse to the nutrient considerations in Wette et al. (1974 a,b). Then the transition probabilities would be different for the two populations of cells, "outer" and "inner", thus setting up a two dimensional process with immigration allowed between the two types of cells. Finally, it has been suggested in the biological literature (see Marchalonis and Gledhill, 1968) that the nature of the immune response is such that there exist cut-off levels in the concentration of antigens below which and above which the immune response no longer operates. If we assume that the concentration of antigens is proportional to the number of tumor cells, then one could postulate a tumor model which behaved like a linear birth and death process for population size less than some value, say MIN, and greater than some other value, say MAX, whereas in between the non-linear immunological feedback mechanism operated, that is

$$n < MIN \rightarrow f_{-1} = \mu n,$$

$$MIN < n < MAX \rightarrow f_{-1} = \mu n + \kappa n^2,$$

$$n > MAX \rightarrow f_{-1} = \mu n.$$

Any of these biologically reasonable assumptions would lead to analytic complications above and beyond those encountered for the now seemingly simple
nonlinear birth and death process which is the main focus of this paper.

As to attempting to verify the model via simulation goodness of fit considerations, as in Hoel and Mitchell (1971), one would need data on the number of cells
per tumor (possibly censored to exclude as yet undetected tumors), unknown dose
functions, possible threshold phenomena, etc. As yet such an endeavor would not
seem possible. Remember, too, that Hoel and Mitchell were dealing with an extremely
simplified situation.

12. Conclusion

Let us consider to what extent our original goal, setting up a mathematical model for the immunological feedback mechanism for carcinogenesis, has been success-ful. The major obstacle to embarking on a goodness of fit testing procedure for experimental data has been the intractability of the differential equations for the nonlinear birth and death process deriving from the immunological feedback model. For this reason an exhaustive study of existing approximation techniques applicable to this stochastic process was undertaken. The only methods that prove valuable are stochastic linearization and the method of linearized transition probabilities. Van Kampen's method yields essentially the same result as stochastic linearization but with considerably more analytical difficulty. What characterizes both approximations that work is that they are generated by a simple argument on the transition probabilities, whereas the other techniques employ a sometimes brute force attack on the differential equations of the process. Stochastic linearization does not yield an approximate stochastic process, only the moments for a state of quasi-equilibrium. Linearized transition probabilities, on the other hand, yield an approximation process that preserves both the discrete, Markovian nature of the exact process and the stationary distribution, which is unique among the approxi-mation techniques considered. Further, the stochastic mean of this approximation coincides with the deterministic equation of the exact model, which result we generalize to all nonlinear birth and death processes. We are also able to formulate an estimate of the expected error in transition probabilities incurred by the approximation. A small simulation study was made, and, although such simulation results are by no means conclusive, they demonstrated a good fit for the mean for a large relative difference $[(\lambda-\mu)/(\lambda+\mu) \approx .74]$ between the parameters λ and μ. The results for the variance were uncertain at best, but at least we can say that the variance, as well as the mean of the approximation, is an overestimate. Further, simulation of the exact process exhibited the hypercellularity that is observed in the development of tumors. Heuristically, then, the immunological response model is appropriate for the biological problem.

Ideally we would want to be in a position to more than just qualitatively verify the immunological response mechanism. Barring explicit solution of the mathematical equations (3, 4) it is necessary to determine the error derived from making inferences from an approximation (in this case, that of linearized transition probabilities) before the goodness of fit of the model could be tested. Of course we could test the goodness of fit of the approximation process to the biological phenomenon without incurring the above type of error. But in order to develop the idea of the model-approximation error, it is necessary to investigate the properties of an approximation to a nonlinear stochastic process for which the differential equations can be solved explicitly. For the case of the quadratic death process we find that the mean and the variance of the approximation do very well and confirm that the approximate mean, variance, and expected error are overestimates, as indicated by the results for the more complicated process involving both births and deaths. In addition to the properties proven in general in the theorem in Chapter 8, we demonstrate the convergence in quadratic mean of the exact process to the mean of the approximation, as well as both $E(\Delta)$ and $\hat{E}(\Delta)$ being asymptotically zero. Note also that the stationary distribution of the approximation agrees with the exact process.

The collective model for immunological feedback is discussed briefly, and several of its properties are derived, but due to analytical complexities we fall short of obtaining even an approximation by linearized transition probabilities. A section is included on the implications derived from substituting the approximation for the exact density, in the probabilities that a tumor is counted and the expected number of so-called "killer tumors". In order to find expressions analogous to those of Neyman and Scott, it is necessary to consider time as finite, which leads to as yet unresolved difficulties. Also discussed in that section are possible biological modifications to the immunological feedback model, all of which are in the direction of mathematical complexity greater than that of the birth and death process with the quadratic death term, whereas at this point clear-cut theoretical results have only been obtained for the more manageable quadratic death process.   Thus we find ourselves in a familiar dilemma, that of biological factors in modelling outstripping in complexity our mathematical capabilities to handle them.   That is why, I suppose, biomathematicians exist.   Onward!

BIBLIOGRAPHY

Albert, R.E. and B. Altshuler (1973). Considerations relating to the formulation of limits for unavoidable population exposures to environmental carcinogens. Radionuclide Carcinogenesis, J.E. Ballou, R.H. Busch, D.D. Mahlum, and C.L. Sanders, Eds., AEC Symposium Series, CONF-72050, NTIS, Springfield, Va.: 233-253.

Alling, D.W. (1971). Estimation of hit number. Biometrics 27, 3:605.

Arley, N. (1961). Theoretical analysis of carcinogenesis. Proceedings of the Fourth Berkeley Symposium on Mathematical Statistics and Probability, University of California Press, Berkeley and Los Angeles, Vol. 4:1.

Arley, N. and S. Iversen (1952). On the mechanism of experimental carcinogenesis. Acta. Path. Microbiol. Scand. 31:164.

Armitage, P. and R. Doll (1954). The age distribution of cancer and a multi-stage theory of carcinogenesis. Brit. J. Cancer, 8:1-12.

Armitage, P. and R. Doll (1957). A two-stage theory of carcinogenesis in relation to the age distribution of human cancer. Brit. J. Cancer, 11:161.

Armitage, P. and R. Doll (1961). Stochastic models for carcinogenesis. Proceedings of the Fourth Berkeley Symposium on Mathematical Statistics and Probability, University of California Press, Berkeley and Los Angeles, Vol. 4:19.

Aroesty, J., T. Lincoln, N. Shapiro, and G. Boccia (1973). Tumor growth and chemotherapy: Mathematical models, computer simulations, and experimental foundations. Math. Biosciences, 17:243.

Bailey, N.T.J. (1963). The simple stochastic epidemic: a complete solution in terms of known functions. Biometrika, 50:235.

Bailey, N.T.J. (1963). The Elements of Stochastic Processes. New York: John Wiley and Company.

Bartlett, M.S. (1955). Stochastic Processes. Cambridge University Press.

Bartlett, M.S., J.C. Gower, and P.H. Leslie (1960). A comparison of theoretical and empirical results for some stochastic population models. Biometrika 47:1.

Bather, J.A. (1963). Two nonlinear birth and death processes. J. Aust. Math. Soc. 3:104.

Berry, G. (1975). Design of carcinogenesis experiments using the Weibull distribution. Biometrika 62:321-328.

Berry, G. and J.C. Wagner (1969). The application of a mathematical model describing the times of occurrence of mesotheliomas in rats following inoculation with asbestos. Brit. J. Cancer 23:582-6.

Bharucha-Reid, A.T. (1960). Elements of the Theory of Markov Processes and Their Applications. New York: McGraw Hill.

Billard, L. (1974). Competition between two species. Stoch. Proc. App. 2:391-398.

Blair, H.A. (1968). Radiation dose-time relations for induction of bone tumors in the dog and skin tumors in the rat. Radiation Res. 34:501-522.

Blum, H.F. (1959). Carcinogenesis by Ultraviolet Light. Princeton University Press, Princeton, N. J.

Blumenson, L.E., and I.D.J. Bross (1969). A mathematical analysis of the growth and spread of breast cancer. Biometrics, 25,1:95.

Buhler, W.J. (1967). Single cell against multicell hypothesis of tumor formation. Proceedings of the Fifth Berkeley Symposium on Mathematical Statistics and Probability, University of California Press, Berkeley and Los Angeles, Vol. 4:635.

Burnet, Sir Macfarlane (1964). Immunological factors in the process of carcinogenesis. Brit. Med. Bull. 20:154.

Chandrasekhar, S. (1943). Stochastic problems in physics and astronomy. Revs. Mod. Phys. 15:1.

Chandrasekhar, S. (1955). A theory of turbulence. Proc. Roy. Soc. A 229:1.

Chang, P.C. (1970). Statistical methods for animal survival time in mouse lymphoma. Biometrics 26, 4:749.

Chapman, D.G. (1971). Notes from Quantitative Science 456: Mathematical Models in Population Biology. Unpublished.

Chow, I.A. (1972). A restricted immigration and death process and its application to the distribution of polymorphonuclear granulocyte density in acute leukemia. Math. Biosciences 13:253.

Chow, Irene A. (1974). A stochastic approach to survival problem with concomitant variables and application to acute leukemia patients. Math. Biosciences 21:103.

Chuang, Shui-Nan, and H.H. Lloyd (1974). Analysis and identification of stochastic compartment models in pharmacokinetics: Implication for cancer chemotherapy. Math. Biosciences 22:57.

Cook, P., R. Doll, and S.A. Fellingham (1961). A mathematical model for the age distribution of cancer in man. Int. J. Cancer 4:93.

Cunningham, W.J. (1958). Introduction to Nonlinear Analysis. New York: Mc Graw Hill.

Doll, R. (1971). The age distribution of cancer: implications for models of carcinogenesis. J.R.S.S. A 134(2):133.

Druckrey, H. (1967). Quantitative aspects of chemical carcinogenesis. Potential Carcinogenic Hazards from Drugs, Evaluation of Risks. UICC Monograph Series 7:60-78.

Feigl, P. and M. Zelen (1965). Estimation of exponential survival probabilities with concomitant information. Biometrics 21:826-838.

Feller, W.J. (1939). Die Grundlagen der Volterraschen Theorie des Kampfe ums Dasein in wahrscheinlechkeitstheoretischer Behandlung. Acta Biotheretica 5:11.

Forsyth, A.R. (1906). Theory of Differential Equations. Part IV, Partial Differential Equations. Cambridge University Press.

Gani, J. (1965). On a partial differential equation of epidemic theory. I. Biometrika 52:617.

Gart, J.J. (1965). Some stochastic models relating time and dosage in response curves. Biometrics 21, 3:583.

Hoel, D.G. and T.J. Mitchell (1971). The simulation, fitting, and testing of a stochastic cellular proliferation model. Biometrics 27, 1:191.

Iversen, O.H. (1965). Cybernetic aspects of the cancer problem. Prog. in Biocybernetics 2:76.

Iyer, K.S.S. and V.N. Saksena (1970). A stochastic model for the growth of cells in cancer. Biometrics 26, 3:401.

Jansson, B. and L. Revesz (1974). Analysis of the growth of tumor cell populations. Math. Biosciences 19:131.

John, P.W.M. (1961). A note on the quadratic birth process. J. London Math. Soc. 36:159.

Kalbfleisch, J.G. and D.A. Sprott (1974). Inferences about hit number in a virological model. Biometrics 30, 1:199.

Karlin, S. (1969). A First Course in Stochastic Processes. Academic Press, New York.

Kendall, D.G. (1948). On the role of variable generation time in the development of a stochastic birth process. Biometrika 35:316.

Kendall, D.G. (1949). Stochastic processes and population growth. JRSS B 11:230.

Kendall, D.G. (1960). Birth-and-death processes, and the theory of carcinogenesis. Biometrika 47:13.

Klonecki, W. (1965). A method for the derivation of probabilities in a stochastic model of population growth for carcinogenesis. Colloq. Math. 13:273.

Klonecki, W. (1970). Identifiability questions for chance mechanisms underlying stochastic models for carcinogenesis. Math. Biosciences 7:365.

Kneale, G.W. (1971). Problems arising in estimating from retrospective survey data the latent periods of juvenile cancers initiated by obstetric radiography. Biometrics 27, 3:563.

Kuzma, J.W., I. Valand and J. Bateman (1969). A tumor cell model for the determination of drug schedules and drug effect in tumor reduction. Bull. Math. Biophysics 31:637.

Lee, P.N. (1970). The simulated population method of analysis of animal painting experiments in cancer research. Biometrics 26, 4:777.

Lee, P.N. and J.A. O'Neill (1971). The effect both of time and dose applied on tumor incidence rate in benzpyrene skin painting experiments. Brit. J. Cancer 25:759.

Linder, D. and S.M. Gartler (1967). Problem of single cell versus multicell origin of a tumor. Proceedings of the Fifth Berkeley Symposium on Mathematical Statistics and Probability, University of California Press, Berkeley and Los Angeles, Vol. 4:625.

Marchalonis, J.J. and V.X. Gledhill (1968). Elementary stochastic model for the induction of immunity and tolerance. Nature 220:608.

Maryuma, Y. and B.W. Brown (1964). The growth of murine lymphomatous tumor-cells as determined by host survival time. Int. J. of Radiation of Biology and Related Studies in Physics, Chemistry and Medicine 8, No. 1:59-73.

Mills, R.A. (1971). Tumor growth and inhibition as transport phenomena: Suggestions for magnetotherapy. Math. Biosciences 11:173.

Moran, P.A.P. (1958). Random processes in genetics. Proc. Camb. Phil. Soc. 54:60.

Neuts, M.F. (1968). Controlling a lethal growth process. Math. Biosciences 2:41.

Neyman, J. and E.L. Scott (1967). Statistical aspect of the problem of carcinogenesis. Proceedings of the Fifth Berkeley Symposium on Mathematical Statistics and Probability, University of California Press, Berkeley and Los Angeles, Vol. 4:745.

Nordling, C.O. (1953). A new theory on the cancer-inducing mechanism. Brit. J. Cancer 7:68.

O'N. Waugh, W.A. (1961). Age-dependence in a stochastic model of carcinogenesis. Proceedings of the Fourth Berkeley Symposium on Mathematical Statistics and Probability, University of California Press, Berkeley and Los Angeles, Vol. 4:405.

Parzen, E. (1962). Stochastic Processes. San Francisco: Holden-Day.

Peto, R. (1974). Guidelines on the analysis of tumor rates and death rates in experimental animals. Brit. J. Cancer 29, 2:101.

Peto, R. and P. Lee (1973). Weibull distributions for continuous-carcinogenesis experiments. Biometrics 29, 3:457.

Peto, R., P.N. Lee and W.S. Paige (1972). Statistical analysis of the bioassay of continuous carcinogens. Brit. J. Cancer 26:258.

Pielou, E.C. (1969). An Introduction to Mathematical Ecology. New York: John Wiley.

Pike, M.C. (1966). A method of analysis of a certain class of experiments in carcinogenesis. Biometrics 22, 1:142.

Pike, M.C. and F.J.C. Roe (1963). An actuarial method of analysis of an experiment in two-stage carcinogenesis. Brit. J. Cancer 17:605.

Prescott, D.M. (1959). Variations in the individual generation times of Tetrahymena geleii hs. Exp. Cell Res. 16:279.

Rosen, G. (1973). Mathematical model for the frequency of radiation carcinogenesis at low doses. Math. Biosciences 18:133.

Rossi, H.H. and A.M. Kellerer (1972). Radiation carcinogenesis at low doses. Science 175:200.

Rubinow, S.I. (1968). A maturity-time representation for cell populations. Biophys. J. 8:1055-1073.

Severo, N.C. (1967). Two theorems on solutions of differential-difference equations and applications to epidemic theory. J. Appl. Prob. 4:271.

Severo, N.C. (1969). The probabilities of some epidemic models. Biometrika 56:197.

Shimkin, M.B. and M.J. Polissar (1955). Some quantitative observations on the induction and growth of primary pulmonary tumors in strain A mice receiving urethane. J. Natl. Cancer Inst. 16:75.

Shimkin, M.B., R. Wieder, D. Margi, N. Gubareff and V. Suntzeff (1967). Lung tumors in mice receiving different schedules of urethane. Proceedings of the Fifth Berkeley Symposium on Mathematical Statistics and Probability. University of California Press, Berkeley and Los Angeles, Vol. 4:707.

Siskind, V. (1965). A solution of the general stochastic epidemic. Biometrika 52:613.

Smith, C.E. and H.C. Tuckwell (1974). Some stochastic growth processes. Mathematical Problems in Biology. Victoria Conference. P. van den Driessche, Ed. Springer-Verlag, New York, Heidelberg, and Berlin, 280 p.

Sneddon, I.N. (1957). Elements of Partial Differential Equations. New York: McGraw Hill.

Stocks, P. (1953). A study of the age curve for cancer of the stomach in connection with a theory of the cancer producing mechanism. Brit. J. Cancer 7:407

Takahashi, M. (1966). Theoretical basis for cell cycle analysis, I. labelled mitosis wave method. J. Theor. Biol. 13:202-211.

Takahashi, M. (1968). Theoretical basis for cell cycle analysis, II. further studies on labelled mitosis wave method. J. Theor. Biol. 18:195-209.

Tallis, G.M. and Sarfaty (1974). On the distribution of the time to reporting cancers with application to breast cancer in women. Math. Biosciences 19:371.

Tucker, H.G. (1961). A stochastic model for a two-stage theory of carcinogenesis. Proceedings of the Fourth Berkeley Symposium on Mathematical Statistics and Probability. University of California Press, Berkeley and Los Angeles, Vol. 4:387.

van Kampen, N.G. (1961). A power series expansion of the master equation. Can. J. Phys. 39:551.

van Kampen, N.G. (1973). Birth and death processes in large populations. Biometrika 60:419.

Weiss, D.W. (1967). Immunology of spontaneous tumors. Proceedings of the Fifth Berkeley Symposium on Mathematical Statistics and Probability, University of California Press, Berkeley and Los Angeles, Vol. 4:657.

Weiss, D.W. (1969). Immunologic parameters of host-tumor relationships: Spontaneous mammary neoplasia of the inbred mouse as a model. Cancer Research 29:2368.

Wette, R., I.N. Katz and E.Y. Rodin (1974a). Stochastic processes for solid tumor kinetics. I. Surface-regulated growth. Math. Biosciences 19:231.

Wette, R., I.N. Katz and R.Y. Rodin (1974b). Stochastic processes for solid tumor kinetics. II. Diffusion-regulated growth. Math. Biosciences 21:311.

White, Margaret R. (1972). Studies of the mechanism of induction of pulmonary adenomas in mice. Proceedings of the Sixth Berkeley Symposium on Mathematical Statistics and Probability. University of California Press, Berkeley and Los Angeles, Vol. 4:287.

Whittle, P. (1957). On the use of the normal approximation in the treatment of stochastic processes. JRSS B 19:268.

Zippin, C. and P. Armitage (1966). Use of concomitant variables and incomplete survival information in the estimation of an exponential survival parameter. Biometrics 22:665-672.

APPENDIX I

Evaluation of the Integral I(t) from van Kampen's Method

To evaluate

$$I(t) = \int \frac{\phi[\frac{(\lambda+\mu)}{(\lambda-\mu)} + \phi]}{2(2\phi-1)} e^{2s} ds,$$

we use the transformation (72),

$$s = -\log \phi(1-\phi) - \log 4$$

to obtain

(185) $\quad I(t) = \frac{1}{32} \int\limits_{\frac{1}{2}}^{\phi} \frac{[\frac{(\lambda+\mu)}{(\lambda-\mu)} + \phi]}{\phi^2(1-\phi)^3} d\phi = \frac{1}{32} \int\limits_{\frac{1}{2}}^{\phi} \frac{(\lambda+\mu)}{(\lambda-\mu)} \cdot \frac{1}{\phi^2(1-\phi)^3} d\phi + \frac{1}{32} \int\limits_{\frac{1}{2}}^{\phi} \frac{1}{\phi(1-\phi)^3} d\phi$

We have

(186)

$$\int\limits_{\frac{1}{2}}^{\phi} \frac{1}{\phi^2(1-\phi)^3} d\phi = \int\limits_{\frac{1}{2}}^{\phi} [\frac{3}{\phi} + \frac{1}{\phi^2} + \frac{3}{(1-\phi)} + \frac{2}{(1-\phi)^2} + \frac{1}{(1-\phi)^3}] d\phi$$

$$= 3 \log(\frac{\phi}{1-\phi}) - \frac{1}{\phi} + \frac{2}{(1-\phi)} + \frac{1}{2(1-\phi^2)} - 4.$$

Also

(187)

$$\int\limits_{0}^{\phi} \frac{1}{\phi(1-\phi)^3} d\phi = \int\limits_{0}^{\phi} [\frac{1}{\phi} + \frac{1}{(1-\phi)} + \frac{1}{(1-\phi)^2} + \frac{1}{(1-\phi)^3}] d\phi$$

$$= \log (\frac{\phi}{1-\phi}) + \frac{1}{1-\phi} + \frac{1}{2(1-\phi)^2} - 4.$$

Direct substitution of (186) and (187) into (185) yields

(188)

$$I(t) = \frac{2\lambda+\mu}{16(\lambda-\mu)} \log (\frac{\phi}{1-\phi}) - \frac{(\lambda+\mu)}{32(\lambda-\mu)} \cdot \frac{1}{\phi} + \frac{(3\lambda+\mu)}{32(\lambda-\mu)} \cdot \frac{1}{1-\phi}$$

$$+ \frac{\lambda}{32(\lambda-\mu)} \cdot \frac{1}{(1-\phi)^2} - \frac{\lambda}{4(\lambda-\mu)},$$

and finally, letting $\phi = \dfrac{e^{(\lambda-\mu)t}}{1 + e^{(\lambda-\mu)t}}$, we obtain

(189)

$$I(t) = \frac{1}{32(\lambda-\mu)} [2(2\lambda+\mu)(\lambda-\mu)t - 5\lambda - (\lambda+\mu)e^{-(\lambda-\mu)t}$$

$$+ (5\lambda+\mu)e^{(\lambda-\mu)t} + \lambda e^{2(\lambda-\mu)t}].$$

APPENDIX II

Derivation of the Probability Density Function Obtained
By the Method of Linearized Transition Probabilities

We want to obtain the probability distribution, $p_n(t)$, $n = 0,1,2,\ldots$ from the probability generating function

$$(190) \quad P(z,t) = 1 + \frac{(\lambda-\mu)}{\dfrac{h_1(t)}{[\dfrac{1}{z-1} - h_2(t)]}}$$

where $h_1(t) = (\lambda-\mu-\kappa)e^{-(\lambda-\mu)t} + \kappa$,

$$h_2(t) = \lambda\kappa t + \frac{\lambda(\lambda-\mu-\kappa)}{(\lambda-\mu)} [1 - e^{-(\lambda-\mu)t}].$$

The above can be rewritten as

$$P(z,t) = \frac{(\lambda-\mu-h_2)z + h - (\lambda-\mu)}{[1 - \dfrac{h_2}{h}]} \cdot \frac{1}{h}$$

(191)

$$= [\frac{(\lambda-\mu-h_2)z + h - (\lambda-\mu)}{h}] [1 + \frac{h_2}{h} z + (\frac{h_2}{h} z)^2 + \ldots].$$

But also $P(z,t) = \sum\limits_{n=0}^{\infty} p_n(t)z^n$, so that the coefficient of the term z^n in (191) will be $p_n(t)$. Accordingly

$$p_0(t) = 1 - \frac{(\lambda-\mu)}{h},$$

$$p_1(t) = (\frac{\lambda-\mu}{h})(1 - \frac{h_2}{h}),$$

$$p_2(t) = (\frac{\lambda-\mu}{h})(\frac{h_2}{h})(1 - \frac{h_2}{h}),$$

and in general for $n \geq 1$,

$$p_n(t) = (\frac{\lambda-\mu}{h})(\frac{h_2}{h})^{n-1} (1 - \frac{h_2}{h}).$$

APPENDIX III

Fortran Program for the Computer Simulation

```
        PROGRAM SIMULA (INPUT,OUTPUT,TAPE5=INPUT,TAPE1)
        REAL LAMBDA,MU,KAPPA
        REAL L,M,K
        INTEGER N
        DIMENSION NUMB (20,50)
        DIMENSION ITOTAL(50)
        DIMENSION STOTAL(50)
        DIMENSION ISUMSQ(50)
        DIMENSION SSUMSQ(50)
        DIMENSION SMEAN(50)
        DIMENSION SVAR(50)
        DIMENSION PXO(50)
        DIMENSION ITOTO(50)
        DIMENSION STOTO(50)
25      READ(5,37) LAMBDA,MU,KAPPA,ISTOP
37      FORMAT(2F6.2,E7.5,58X,I3)
        L=LAMBDA
        M=MU
        K=KAPPA
C--RANDOM NUMBER GENERATOR

        MEW=0
        OCT=12345
        NRN=1
        CALL TAUS(D,NRN,OCT,NEW)
        NRN=1
        NEW=1
49      DO 83 IFLAG=1,20
        T=1,0
        N=1
        NUMB(IFLAG,1)=1
        DO 3 JTIME=1,50
        ITOTAL(JTIME)=0
        ISUMSQ(JTIME)=0
        ITOTO(JTIME)=0
3       CONTINUE
        CALL TAUS(RANDOM,NRN,FIRST,NEW)
        RANDOM=ABS(RANDOM)
54      EVENT=-ALOG(RANDOM/((LAMBDA+MU)*N+KAPPA*N*N)
        PBIRTH=LAMBDA/(LAMBDA+MU+KAPPA*N)
        PDEATH=(MU+KAPPA*N)/(LAMBDA+MU+KAPPA*N)
        CUT1=PBIRTH
        T=T+EVENT
50      DO 85 ITIME=1,50
        IF (N.EQ.0) GO TO 184
        TIME=ITIME
        IF (T.GT.TIME) TO TO 86
        CALL TAUS(RANDM2,NRN,FIRST,NEW)
        RANDM2=ABS(RANDM2)
        IF (RANDM2.LT.CUT1) GO TO 61
62      N=N-1
        GO TO 70
61      N=N+1
70      CONTINUE
```

```
 84    NUMB(IFLAG,ITIME)=N
119    IF(N.EQ.0) GO TO 85
       CALL TAUS(RANDOM,NRN,FIRST,NEW)
       RANDOM=ABS(RANDOM)
154    EVENT=-ALOG(RANDOM)/((LAMBDA+MU)*N+KAPPA*N*N)
       PBIRTH=LAMBDA/(LAMBDA+MU+KAPPA*N)
       PDEATH=(MU+KAPPA*N)/(LAMBDA+MU+KAPPA*N)
       CUT1=PBIRTH
       T=T+EVENT
       IF  (T.GT.TIME) TO TO 85
       CALL TAUS(RANDM2,NRN,FIRST,NEW)
       RANDM2=ABS(RANDM2)
200    IF (RANDM2.LT.CUT1) GO TO 261
262    N=N-1
       GO TO 270
261    N=N+1
270    CONTINUE
284    NUMB(IFLAG, ITIME)=N
       GO TO 119
 86    CONTINUE
184    NUMB(IFLAG,ITIME)=N
 85    CONTINUE
 83    CONTINUE
       DO 301 LFLAG=1,20
       DO 302 LTIME=1,50
       ITOTAL(LTIME)=ITOTAL(LTIME)+NUMB(LFLAG,LTIME)
       ISUMSQ(LTIME)=ISUMSQ(LTIME)+NUMB(LFLAG LTIME)*NUMB(LFLAG,LTIME)
       N+NUMB(LFLAG,LTIME)
       IF (N.EQ.0) GO TO 400
       GO TO 401
400    ITOTO(LTIME)=ITOTO(LTIME)+1
401    CONTINUE
302    CONTINUE
301    CONTINUE
       DO 90 KTIME=1,50
       STOTAL(KTIME)=ITOTAL(KTIME)
       SSUMSQ(KTIME)=ISUMSQ(KTIME)
       STOTO(KTIME)=ITOTO(KTIME)
       SMEAN(KTIME)=STOTAL(KTIME)/20.
       SVAR(KTIME)=(SSUMSQ(KTIME)-20.0*SMEAN(KTIME)*SMEAN(KTIME))/19.0
       PXO(KTIME)=STOTO(KTIME)/20.0
       T=KTIME-1
       XMEAN=SMEAN(KTIME)
       XVAR=SVAR(KTIME)
       PRXO=PXO(KTIME)
       TAU=(L-M)*T
       AMEAN=(L-M)/((L-M-K)*EXP(-TAU)+K)
       AVAR=(2.*L*K*(TAU-1.)+(L-M)*(L+M+K)-(L+M)*(L-M-K)*EXP(-TAU))/(((L-
2M-K)*EXP(-TAU))**2)
       H=K*(L-M)*(L*T+1.)+(L-M-K)*(L-M*EXP(-TAU))
       PRAO=1.0-((L-M)*(L-M))/H
       WRITE(1) T,XMEAN,XVAR,AMEAN,AVAR,PRXO,PRAO
 90    CONTINUE
       IF (ISTOP.EQ.999) GO TO 91
       GO TO 25
 91    CONTINUE
       ENDFILE 1
```

APPENDIX IV

Mathematical Induction for the Probability Density of the General Death Process

Assume that

$$
P_n = c_n e^{-\mu_n t} + \sum_{i=0}^{M-n-1} \frac{[\prod_{j=n+1}^{M-i} \mu_j] c_{M-i} e^{-\mu_{M-i} t}}{[\prod_{j=n}^{M-i-1} (\mu_j - \mu_{M-i})]},
$$

(192)

$$
c_n = - \sum_{i=0}^{M-n-1} \frac{[\prod_{j=n+1}^{M-i} \mu_j] c_{M-i}}{[\prod_{j=n}^{M-i-1} (\mu_j - \mu_{M-i})]}
$$

Then we must show that

$$
P_{n-1} = c_{n-1} e^{-\mu_{n-1} t} + \sum_{i=0}^{M-n} \frac{[\prod_{j=n}^{M-i} \mu_j] c_{M-i} e^{-\mu_{M-i} t}}{[\prod_{j=n-1}^{M-i-1} (\mu_j - \mu_{M-i})]}
$$

(193)

$$
c_{n-1} = - \sum_{i=0}^{M-n} \frac{[\prod_{j=n}^{M-i} \mu_j] c_{M-i}}{[\prod_{j=n-1}^{M-i-1} (\mu_j - \mu_{M-i})]}.
$$

From (126) we know that

$$
\frac{dp_{n-1}}{dt} = \mu_n p_n - \mu_{n-1} p_{n-1}
$$

Using (192) this becomes

$$(194) \quad \frac{dp_{n-1}}{dt} + \mu_{n-1}p_{n-1} = \mu_n c_n e^{-\mu_n t} + \mu_n \sum_{i=0}^{M-n-1} \frac{[\prod\limits_{j=n+1}^{M-i} \mu_j]c_{M-i} e^{-\mu_{M-i}t}}{[\prod\limits_{j=n}^{M-i-1} (\mu_j - \mu_{M-i})]}.$$

We see immediately that p_{n-1} will be of the form

$$(195) \quad p_{n-1} = \sum_{i=0}^{M-n+1} a_{M-i} e^{-\mu_{M-i}t},$$

and so

$$(196) \quad \frac{dp_{n-1}}{dt} + \mu_{n-1}p_{n-1} = \sum_{i=0}^{M-n+1} a_{M-i}(\mu_{n-1} - \mu_{M-i})e^{-\mu_{M-i}t}.$$

Equating in the right hand sides of (194) and (196) coefficients of $e^{-\mu_{M-i}t}$, we have for $i = M - n + 1$,

$$a_{n-1}(\mu_{n-1} - \mu_{n-1}) = 0.$$

The constant a_{n-1} will be determined from boudnary conditions. For $i = M - n$, we have

$$a_n(\mu_{n-1} - \mu_n) = \mu_n c_n,$$

which implies that

$$(197) \quad a_n = \frac{\mu_n c_n}{(\mu_{n-1} - \mu_n)} = \frac{[\prod\limits_{j=n}^{n} \mu_j]c_n}{[\prod\limits_{j=n-1}^{n-1} (\mu_j - \mu_n)]}.$$

For $0 < i < M-n$, we find

$$(198) \quad a_{M-i} = \frac{[\prod\limits_{j=n+1}^{M-i} \mu_j]c_{M-i}}{[\prod\limits_{j=n}^{M-i-1} (\mu_j - \mu_{M-i})]}.$$

Equations (197) and (198) substitute into (196) to yield

$$p_{n-1} = a_{n-1} e^{-\mu_{n-1}t} + \sum_{i=0}^{M-n-1} \frac{[\prod\limits_{j=n+1}^{M-i} \mu_j] c_{M-i} e^{-\mu_{M-i}t}}{[\prod\limits_{j=n+1}^{M-i-1} (\mu_j - \mu_{M-i})]}.$$

At $t = 0$, $p_{n-1} = 0$ for $n-1 < M$, so that

$$a_{n-1} = - \sum_{i=0}^{M-n-1} \frac{[\prod\limits_{j=n+1}^{M-i} \mu_j] c_{M-i}}{[\prod\limits_{j=n+1}^{M-i-1} (\mu_j - \mu_{M-i})]}.$$

Set $c_{n-1} = a_{n-1}$ to obtain the result (193).

APPENDIX V

Iterative Routine in Fortran for the Quadratic Death Process

```
        PROGRAM QDEATH (INPUT,OUTPUT,TAPE5=INPUT,TAPE1)
        REAL M
        INTEGER T
        INTEGER S
        DIMENSION P(51,100),C(51),PROD1(51,51),PROD2(51,51)
        DIMENSION XMEAN(100),XSQ(100),SVAR(100),AMEAN(100),AVAR(100)
        DIMENSION EDEL(100),EHATDL(100)
        DIMENSION PO(100)
        READ(5,37) M
     37 FORMAT(F10.0)
        MAX=25,MAXU=MAX-1
        C(MAX)=1.0
        CO=1.0
C               THIS DO LOOP GENERATES PROD1,PROD2
        DO 1 J=1,MAX
        DO 2 I=1,J
        PROD1(I,J)=1.0
        PROD2(I,J)=1.0
        DO 3 K=I,J
        PROD1(I,J)=K*K*PROD1(I,J)
        PROD2(I,J)=(K*K-(J+1)*PROD2(I,J)
      3 CONTINUE
      2 CONTINUE
      1 CONTINUE
C          C(N) IS GENERATED NOW
        DO 4 N=1,MAXU
        MAXUU=MAX-N
        C(MAXUU)=0.
        DO 5 IR=1,N
        I=IR-1
        C(MAXUU)=C(MAXUU)-C(MAX-I)*PROD1(MAXUU+1,MAX-1)/PROD2(MAXUU,MAX-I-1)
      5 CONTINUE
      4 CONTINUE
C         P(N,T) IS NEXT
        DO 6 T=1,50
        S=T-1
        DO 7 N=1,MAXU
        Y=N*N*S
        Z=-M*Y
        P(N,T)=C(N)*EXP(Z)
        N1=N+1
        DO 8 I=N1,MAX
        Y=I*I*S
        Z=-M*Y
        P(N,T)=P(N,T)+C(I)*EXP(Z)*PROD1(N+1,I)/PROD2(N,I-1)
      8 CONTINUE
      7 CONTINUE
      6 CONTINUE
C           P(MAX,T) AND PO(T) NOW
        DO 9 T=1,50
        S=T-1
        Y=MAX*MAX*S
        Z=-M*Y
        P(MAX,T)=C(MAX)*EXP(Z)
```

```
         Y1=S
         Z1=-M*Y1
         PO(T)=C0-C(1)*EXP(Z1)
         DO 10 I=2,MAX
         Y=I*I*S
         Z=-M*Y
         PO(T)=PO(T)-PROD1(2,I)*C(I)*EXP(Z)/((I*I)*PROD2(1,I-1) )
   10    CONTINUE
    9    CONTINUE
C        HERE COME XMEAN AND XSQ
         DO 11 T=1,50
         S=T-1
         XMEAN(T)=0.
         XSQ(T)=0
         DO 12 N=1,MAX
         XMEAN(T)=XMEAN(T)+P(N,T)*N
         XSQ(T)=XSQ(T)+P(N,T)*N*N
   12    CONTINUE
         CONTINUE
C            FOLLOWED BY XVAR
         DO 13 T=1,50
         S=T-1
         XVAR(T)=XSQ(T)-XMEAN(T)*XMEAN(T)
   13    CONTINUE
             THE APPROXIMATIONS BRING UP THE REAR
         DO 14 T=1,50
         S=T-1
         AMEAN(T)=MAX/(M*MAX*S+1.)
         AVAR(T)=(M*MAX*MAX*S)/((M*MAX*S+1.)**2)
   14    CONTINUE
C        EDEL AND EHATDL FOR THE QUADRATIC DEATH PROCESS
         DO 15 T=1,50
         S=T-1
         EDEL(T)=M*SVAR(T)+M*(XMEAN(T)**2)-M*XMEAN(T)*AMEAN(T)
         EHATDL(T)=M*AVAR(T)
   15    CONTINUE
C              FINAL DO LOOP AFTER 15 CONTINUE
         DO 16 T=1,50
         S=T-1
         EXMEAN=SMEAN(T)
         EXVAR=XVAR(T)
         PRXO=PO(T)
         PRAO=((M*MAX*S)/(M*MAX*S+1.0))**MAX
         APMEAN=AMEAN(T)
         APVAR=AVAR(T)
         EDELT=EDEL(T)
         APEDEL=EHATDL(T)
         WRITE(1) S,EXMEAN,EXVAR,PRXO,PRAO,APMEAN,APVAR,EDELT,APEDEL
   16    CONTINUE
         ENDFILE 1
         END
```